The Raw Milk Answer Book

What You REALLY Need to Know About Our Most Controversial Food

By David E. Gumpert

To Larry,
With much appreciation
for all your support,
and your friendship.
Warm regards,
David E. Gumpert
March 25, 2013

Published by Lauson Publishing Co.

Needham, MA

Proofreading: Sharon Zecchinelli, Doreen Hannes

Editorial assistance: Shana Milkie

Cover design: Carol Kiser

Table of Contents

Introduction

Raw milk has become the world's most controversial food.

As a result, obtaining accurate information about it has become increasingly difficult. On one side, proponents often portray raw milk as a miracle food. In their view, it strengthens the immune system so as to reduce our incidence of health problems small and large--from colds and flu to cancer and diabetes. They also see it as clearing up eczema, mitigating autism symptoms, and protecting against asthma and allergies...and being extremely safe to boot.

On the other side, opponents portray raw milk as having no more health or nutritional value than the pasteurized variety that can be bought in any supermarket. They also view it as one of the most dangerous foods known to mankind--so inherently dangerous it can kill you. In other words, a food no one should ever consume.

Obviously, both sides can't be correct. What is the real story?

In this book I have tried to provide the real story by answering more than 200 of the most common questions that come up about raw milk. I have tried to be as objective and fair as possible. I took the question-and-answer approach because, whenever I tell people that I write and report about raw milk, I am nearly always asked a long list of questions.

For example:

-Is it safe?

-Is it really healthier than pasteurized milk?

-Can I get the same nutritional benefits by drinking pasteurized organic milk?

-Is pasteurized milk that isn't homogenized as nutritious as raw milk?

-Is raw milk legal to sell in my state?

-How do I locate a source to buy it from?

-What is a herd share or cow share arrangement?

-How do I determine if a particular dairy is producing safe raw milk?

-Can I tolerate raw milk if I have trouble digesting pasteurized milk?

-Should I serve raw milk to my children to improve their health?

-Will it help my children's eczema?

-Why is there so much conflict about whether raw milk should be legal?

-What if my spouse and I adamantly disagree about serving raw milk to our family?

On and on the questions go.

Invariably, the answer to one question leads to several others. For example, if I tell you raw milk can't be legally sold in your state or country, then you may wonder where and how you can obtain it. That sometimes leads into discussion of herd share arrangements. What is a herd share?

And oftentimes those questions lead into political discussions. "You mean I have to join a herd share and travel two hours to a farm to get raw milk? Why can't I just buy it at the supermarket like other foods?"

Yes, there are many questions about the particulars of raw milk, but I should answer one fundamental question immediately: Why is a book necessary to help decide whether to consume a particular food? We don't have books (beyond recipe books) to help people decide whether they want to eat hamburgers or peanut butter or cantaloupe or raw spinach or even pasteurized milk, even though each of these foods has made many people, including children, very sick, and actually killed some. (In 2011 and 2012 alone, 308 people were sickened and 39 killed in the U.S……by tainted cantaloupe [1].)

But raw, or unpasteurized, milk has become a special food category, a political football of sorts that has been at once demonized and glorified. In the U.S., it is the only food that is prohibited from interstate commerce (being sold from one state to people in another). (For background about the political history of raw milk, I suggest you refer to my two other books on food rights: *The Raw Milk Revolution* [2] and *Life, Liberty, and the Pursuit of Food Rights* [3].)

So polarized has the debate become, and so intractable are the positions, that individuals trying to make an informed decision about whether to commit to raw milk aren't sure what to do. They feel as if they can't believe either their government health authorities, such as the scientists at the U.S. Centers for Disease Control (CDC) and the U.S. Food and Drug Administration (FDA), or any of the many advocates you find on the Internet. (Google "raw milk" and you'll get 36 million hits.)

Why is that? See what I mean? Okay, let's get started...

Chapter 1: Raw Milk Basics

Raw milk fascinates us. It is at once super natural and super exotic. Natural because it is our first food, usually from our mothers, and then from cows or goats. Exotic because most of us have grown up knowing only the processed variety of milk (via pasteurization and homogenization), so the idea of consuming it unprocessed, in its natural state directly as it emerges from a cow or goat, goes against what we have been told is either normal or safe. Suddenly this natural food becomes something new and forbidden. Ah yes, forbidden fruit.

What is raw milk, exactly?

Raw milk is milk as it comes directly from the cow, ostensibly to nurse her calves. The calves are usually removed shortly after birth, and the cow's milk diverted for humans. It comes complete with naturally occurring bacteria, enzymes, and proteins.

Most farmers immediately cool raw milk to about 40 degrees (F) to minimize the multiplication of the naturally occurring bacteria, and then keep it refrigerated. But milk distributed raw doesn't go through any of the processing that occurs to most commercially sold milk, including pasteurization, fractionating, homogenization, and standardization to consistent protein and fat concentrations.

You can easily tell raw cow's milk from commercially processed homogenized milk by looking at their respective glass jars after they have been sitting for a couple hours or more. The raw milk shows an inch or more of cream at the top, the so-called "cream line," while the pasteurized and homogenized milk is unchanged.

Isn't it possible to get raw milk from other animals?

Absolutely. Goat milk is increasing in popularity, along with cow milk. Goat milk can be easier for farmers to produce, since goats are smaller animals, and thus easier to handle and feed.

Moreover, some people prefer goat milk to cow milk, since it is naturally homogenized (thus no cream rising to the top), and is lower in saturated fat than cow milk. Those who prefer it say it has a cleaner taste.

I have had goat milk a number of times, and enjoy it. Because goats do more foraging for food, and aren't just eating grass or hay, like cows, goat milk can sometimes take on a variety of tastes, what I refer to as a "barnyard" taste.

Sheep milk is becoming increasingly popular, though in my experience, much of it is used to make cheese. Sheep don't produce a huge amount of milk compared to cows and goats, and their milk imparts a rich, delicate taste to creamy camembert-type cheeses.

More recently, we have begun seeing options for obtaining milk from camels. Yes, I'm serious. Camel milk has been popular in the Middle East for hundreds of years. Like in the U.S., the unpasteurized variety has been viewed by certain segments of people as an antidote to chronic immune-related illnesses like diabetes and asthma, and even to autism. Because there are so few camels and they give much less milk per animal than cows and goats, the milk tends to be very expensive, $100 and more per gallon. More on that in Chapter 5.

I generally try in the supermarket to buy Horizon or Organic Valley organic milk. Is that raw milk?

Welcome to the complex world of milk labeling. As this question suggests, there is lots of confusion over "raw" versus "organic" milk. Mark McAfee of Organic Pastures Dairy Co., the country's largest producer of raw milk, once observed: "Most people who approach a farmers market table are very confused and do not know the difference between organic and raw... I have even heard some people say that they love the super long-lasting fresh flavor of raw milk because when they get Horizon ultra-pasteurized organic raw milk, it lasts for two months or longer!!!"

McAfee's point is that organic milk you buy in the supermarket is about as far from raw milk as you can get. While the cows may have been fed organic feed, so their milk can be labeled "Organic", most organic milk in the supermarket is not only pasteurized, it is pasteurized at higher temperatures than ordinary pasteurized milk (up to 280 degrees, for at least two seconds, known as *ultra-high-temperature*, or *UHT*, pasteurized, versus 161 or 171 degrees for up to 18 seconds for traditionally pasteurized milk), to kill off practically all bacteria (including harmless and beneficial bacteria) so that the resulting milk is lacking in active bacteria and enzymes of any sort. The retailers love it, since it lasts for up to two months in the refrigerator, or even longer if packaged in special aseptic packaging, without putrefying.

The UHT pasteurizing is common in Europe and Asia, and becoming more common in the U.S.

I should also point out that the idea that a natural food like milk could be processed and still be considered organic was vigorously opposed as contradictory by America's organic pioneers from the 1940s to the 1970s. But when the U.S. Department of Agriculture's National Organic Program standards were written in the 1990s, they allowed milk that was pasteurized (and homogenized) to be labeled "organic."

Why would processors subject organic milk to more intense processing than much conventional milk?

Organic dairies tend to be widely dispersed geographically. This means organic milk often needs to be transported longer distances than conventional milk, sometimes even from one region of the U.S. to another, to fill demand everywhere. The UHT pasteurization allows the organic milk to sit longer before it is consumed than milk pasteurized the traditional way.

But there is also a trend toward more intense processing aside from pasteurization. In 2014, Coca-Cola announced introduction of Fairlife milk [1], which was notable for having also gone through what Coke said was a special filtration process that provided for more protein and calcium and less milk sugar than ordinary milk.

I've also seen ads for milk that is "minimally pasteurized" or "gently pasteurized." How does this differ from regularly pasteurized milk?

Yes, more confusion. In an effort to market milk that seems more "natural" and healthy, some dairies have touted their milk as "gently pasteurized" or "minimally pasteurized." What this generally means is that it is pasteurized at the minimal allowable FDA requirements—161 degrees Fahrenheit for at least 15 seconds (technically referred to as high-temperature short-time (HTST) pasteurization. This is a bit less intense than pasteurization used by some processors in which milk is pasteurized at 171 degrees F for 18 seconds.

There is also a more modest method of pasteurization approved by the FDA, sometimes referred to as "low-temperature pasteurization," where the milk is heated to 145 degrees for 30 minutes. Essentially, the milk is heated at a slightly lower temperature, but for a much longer period of time, than traditionally pasteurized milk. This means of pasteurizing is used most often by home-based or very small milk producers.

Some of the pasteurized brands are even saying their cows are grass-fed, and the milk non-homogenized (there is one widely distributed brand that advertises "Grass Milk," where the cows eat only grass and the milk is pasteurized and not homogenized). Does this make the milk better than conventional milk?

The most natural food for cows is grass, either out on the pasture or as hay. Conversely, the grain feed diets most cows are fed at the huge dairies that predominate in the U.S. are considered unnatural for cows, but such diets are often used because most cows are kept in crowded pens known as CAFOs (for concentrated animal feeding operations). The grain-based feeding the dairies use is a cheap substitute (especially in land costs, as well as labor to tend to the cows) for the vast pasture where cows once grazed (and still do in places like New Zealand, Australia, and parts of Europe).

It's also thought that grass-fed cows provide milk with

higher levels of such desirable nutrients as linoleic acid and beta carotene. (For more information, see Chapter 3 on raw milk nutrition.)

As for non-homogenized milk, it often tastes creamier than conventional milk, likely because little or none of the cream has been taken from the milk in the normal fractionating process that is part of the larger dairy processing system. Moreover, the non-homogenized milk has not been subject to the extreme spinning and shaking that is part of breaking up the milk's fat globules into equal-size parts, so they don't break apart from the milk and separate and float to the top. Some milk purists feel that homogenization has made milk less healthy by making the fat less easily absorbable by the body.

While the non-homogenized milk that has been pasteurized will usually taste creamier, it also tends to have the slightly "cooked" flavor of pasteurized milk.

Come to think of it, I don't remember seeing raw milk as one of the choices in the supermarket. Am I missing something?

Only ten states allow retail sale of raw milk (including California, Connecticut, Pennsylvania, New Hampshire, and Maine), but you generally won't see it in large supermarkets even in those states. Large supermarket chains mostly avoid raw milk, even if it is legal in a particular state, because of supermarket policies that prohibit raw milk under any circumstances. You are more likely to find it in health food stores or cooperative food stores. And in most other parts of the country, it's only available directly from farms. (More on raw milk regulation in Chapter 7.)

In Europe, similarly, raw milk tends to be carried mostly in specialized food stores. But increasingly, it is being sold via vending machines in places like Italy, Switzerland, France, Poland, and Slovenia.

So all milk, before it is pasteurized, is raw, right?

Technically, that is correct. But in the context in which I am discussing unpasteurized milk here, it is important to distinguish between milk that is produced with the intention of being served raw, which some people refer to as "fresh milk," and milk that is produced with the intention of being pasteurized before being consumed, which some people refer to as "pre-pasteurized milk".

Why is that distinction important?

Producers of pre-pasteurized milk, from commercial dairies, don't have to worry about people getting sick from pathogens that might be present in the milk when it leaves the farm, since the milk will be heated to required pasteurization levels to kill the pathogens. Indeed, testing of pre-pasteurized milk from mostly large dairies (500 or more cows) has, in a number of dairy industry and other studies, been shown to not uncommonly contain one or more of the pathogens that can make people sick when it leaves the farm.

And pasteurization fixes that problem, right?

Let's say that heating the milk to 161 degrees for 15 seconds kills off the most common pathogens, including the four that comprise today's most frequent sources of foodborne illness—*Salmonella*, *Campylobacter*, *Listeria*, and *Escherichia coli* (*E. coli*) O157:H7.

However, pasteurization also kills off many other bacteria in the milk, which aren't harmful, and some of which may be beneficial. Scientists might describe it as a 5-log reduction of bacteria, as opposed to sterilization.

All milk, before processing, contains not only a number of harmless bacteria, but a variety of enzymes and special proteins unique to milk.

So people can't get sick from drinking pasteurized milk?

Not exactly. People can and do get sick from drinking pasteurized milk...if the pasteurizing equipment doesn't work right or if there is contamination in the bottling or other post-pasteurization processes or if the pre-pasteurization levels of pathogens was extremely high. Such occurrences are rare; I discuss illnesses from pasteurized and unpasteurized milk at greater length in Chapter 6.

Chapter 2: Why All the Fuss?

We are seeing a huge amount of interest by growing numbers of people in eating healthier. Dozens of books and documentaries are coming out each year to inform us about problems in what is often referred to as the "factory" food system.

A 2014 Gallup poll found [1] that 45% of Americans actively seek out organic food in their diets--an astounding figure when you consider that thirty years ago, organic food was pretty much on the fringes of American eating habits. Millions have voted for propositions that would require the labeling of genetically modified (GMO) foods (though the propositions lost by small amounts). New types of fast-food chains, like Chipotle, have been growing like crazy with their promise of fresh, healthy food. Farmers markets are booming.

The interest in wholesome food shows no signs of abating.

Is this interest in healthy food what is propelling the huge amount of interest in raw milk?

The interest in raw milk is part and parcel of the growing interest in nutrient-rich foods, which are produced without genetically modified ingredients, in their most natural state. Such foods would include not only locally raised vegetables and fruits, but eggs from chickens allowed on pasture and not given soy feed (most of which is GMO), meats from animals slaughtered on the farm or nearby, and fermented foods like sauerkraut. In other words, foods that haven't been part of the factory farming system and its emphasis on processing, mass production, and routine use of GMO ingredients like soy and corn.

Beyond that, advocates say raw milk is healthier and more nutritious than pasteurized milk, that it helps children and adults alike strengthen their immune systems and protect against serious conditions like asthma and allergies. This same view holds for fermented dairy (and vegetables), like kefir and yogurt.

But there doesn't seem to be as much controversy for those other foods as around raw milk. Why the big deal about raw milk?

America's public health establishment—the U.S. Food and Drug Administration and the U.S. Centers for Disease Control—adamantly opposes raw milk as too risky, especially for children. (One FDA official has been frequently quoted as saying, "Drinking raw milk is like playing Russian roulette with your health.") They, along with state and local public health agencies, not only recommend that people avoid raw milk, but they have pushed legislative and legal actions to limit people's access to raw milk. These actions include court orders and even criminal charges against farmers producing raw milk.

But there are other foods that get people sick. What is it about raw milk that seems to raise so much of an objection?

I am often asked this question during media interviews. I tell interviewers that, at its heart, milk is an emotionally-charged food. It is our first food, coming directly from our mothers. Then most of us graduate to cow milk.

The fact that children are big consumers also gives it an emotional component, especially if children get sick. That was a big problem during the late 1800s and early 1900s, when thousands became ill, and many died. Many fewer children become sick from raw milk today, but it still does happen very occasionally. When it does, it tends to get a lot of attention from the public health community and the media.

Is all the controversy scaring people away from raw milk?

It's difficult to be certain, since there is little in the way of hard data about ongoing raw milk consumption. All the controversy definitely stirs up media interest. There have been seemingly endless media stories about raw milk. Some warn about its supposedly terrible dangers, and highlight cases of people becoming very sick from raw milk. Others highlight its supposedly amazing healing qualities, and profile individuals presenting glowing reports of improved health.

In states around the country that don't allow raw milk sales, from Maryland to New Jersey to Louisiana to Iowa, legislation has been introduced in recent years to allow raw milk on a limited basis, directly from dairy farms. The proposals often don't pass because of intense opposition from a coalition of public health officials, the medical community, and the dairy industry, but the media attention to the legislative proposals spreads the word further about raw milk to people who know little or nothing about it.

If so much of the media coverage is negative, warning about raw milk's supposed dangers, why is there growing interest in it?

While the controversy has no doubt scared some people off, it has also made many people curious—curious enough that they want to learn more about this tantalizing food that stirs up such completely contradictory assessments from very bright and knowledgeable people.

Why would large numbers of people ignore warnings from the top public health experts in the country?

The main reason I can think of is that increasing numbers of people have become distrustful of America's health establishment. The FDA, in particular, has approved drugs for wide use that were subsequently found to be dangerous. Classic cases involve painkillers like Vioxx and Celebrex, which were found to cause serious heart problems in some patients.

As a result, some people have developed a completely contrarian attitude: If the FDA says a particular drug or food is good, it must be bad...and if the FDA says a food is bad, well, it must be good. In these people's minds, if the FDA says raw milk is very dangerous, that must mean it isn't dangerous, and may well be good for you.

Also, there is growing cynicism that the FDA, along with many physicians, is in bed with big drug companies and big food corporations. Thus, some people rationalize that if the FDA is warning against raw milk, it must mean the FDA is under the influence of major milk producers.

And there is growing concern about the production

practices of large food corporations. One big concern is over what seems to be the over-use of antibiotics in raising farm animals like chickens, pigs, and cattle, and indications that super-bugs resistant to antibiotics for people are moving from factory farms to our hospitals, sports clubs, and other places.

Finally, there is a sense that food obtained from small local farms is produced with fewer chemicals and factory techniques, and thus is safer than mass-produced food.

How does the popularity of raw milk express itself?

Nearly without exception, producers of raw milk say they have difficulty keeping up with demand. Organic Pastures Dairy Co. of California, the largest raw milk producer in the country, says demand has been growing at about 20 per cent per year since 2006. Some farmers say they can't produce enough for all the people who want it, and have wait lists for individuals who desire to become regular customers.

Private food clubs that have been organized in cities and suburbs around the country sometimes can't accept new members, because the clubs can't guarantee adequate supplies.

That has led to situations where people who badly need or want raw milk either can't obtain it, or must travel two hours or more to obtain it.

With all this demand for raw milk, is there any indication of a moderating of views by the public health and medical establishments, that they are becoming more accepting of raw milk?

Actually, there have been some indications of a moderating of views. I wrote an article [2] on my blog in 2013 about a prominent public health researcher at the University of California, Davis, deciding that raw milk wasn't inherently dangerous, as she once thought. In early 2014, I engaged in a podcast debate [3] with two food-safety professors, one of whom was the head of the American Association for Food Protection; this was a public discussion that would have been unthinkable even two or three years earlier. Also in early 2014, a conference about raw milk at a prominent Canadian university (Canada's public health people are as fervently anti-raw-milk as their American counterparts) featured statements from public health people who had once been adamantly against raw milk that perhaps there should be a re-consideration.

Perhaps most notably, a panel of three public health researchers from Johns Hopkins University in late 2014 advocated a moderating of views. In response to a request from the Maryland House of Delegates, which held contentious hearings earlier in the year about legislation to legalize herd shares in the state, the Johns Hopkins researchers produced "A Literature Review of the Risks and Benefits of Consuming Raw and Pasteurized Cow's Milk." [4] In a wrapup of the 36-page analysis, the authors referred "to the continuing disagreements of raw milk proponents and federal regulatory agencies." Their conclusion: "While we understand the positions of both groups, we strongly believe that both parties would gain much by being willing to discuss and compromise on their positions."

Does this thawing in relations between opponents and proponents of raw milk extend to the FDA or CDC?

Unfortunately, as raw milk has become increasingly popular, it has become ever more demonized by our government and medical establishments. As one example, the American Academy of Pediatrics in late 2013 came out with a policy statement [5] advocating a complete ban of raw milk in the U.S.—a more extreme recommendation than any medical group had ever made.

As another example, the U.S. Centers for Disease Control in 2012 and 2013 sponsored a first-of-its-kind study in Minnesota [6] to try to prove there were many more illnesses from raw milk than were officially reported; the CDC has long argued that there are many more incidents of illness from foods of all kinds than are officially reported and tabulated by local public health officials—it even officially estimates [7] the number in total (some 48 million estimated annual illnesses rather than the officially reported 15,000).

But the CDC has never applied this logic to a particular food, until it came out with the Minnesota study. The fact that it chose raw milk—a food consumed by a tiny percentage of the population—to explore how many unreported illnesses there might be spoke to a fixation, some might say its obsession, with raw milk's growing popularity, and the official desire to demonize it in every way possible. And, predictably, the CDC's study concluded that the officially reported 21 illnesses from raw milk over the first decade of this century in Minnesota was way too low; in its new estimation, there were more than 20,000 illnesses from raw milk over the decade.

Wouldn't the dairy industry be attracted to raw milk, as an additional product it could sell?

You might think so, especially since sales of pasteurized milk have been in a slow but steady 40-year decline,... to the point that fewer than half of all adults now drink pasteurized milk (according to data from the U.S. Department of Agriculture [8]).But there are a few factors that work against this logic. First, the dairy industry is organized around processing—pasteurization and homogenization. The billions of dollars it has invested in all the processing equipment, which it wants operating as much as possible, would not be of use for raw milk, which requires no processing.

Second, the milk produced by most dairies isn't always produced under the most sanitary conditions, since it is intended for processing, and not for being consumed raw. Knowing their milk will be processed and pathogens will be killed allows dairies to pay less attention to sanitation and what the cows are fed than if the milk was being consumed unpasteurized.

Third, the dairy industry is essentially an oligopoly. Just a few corporations and cooperatives control most of the marketplace. In most areas of the country, dairies have just one processor to sell to, so the normal dynamics of competition, like selling your product to the highest bidder, don't apply. Not surprisingly, the big processors like Dean Foods prefer that kind of situation to a normal competitive marketplace, where raw milk is being sold directly by farmers to consumers or to retail outlets. Thus, they fear competition from many small farms selling raw milk directly into the marketplace, and fight tooth and nail against proposed legislation improving its availability.

Couldn't individual dairies simply leave the existing processing system, and switch over to selling directly to consumers clamoring for raw milk?

It isn't a simple matter for conventional dairies, even if they want to sell directly to consumers, outside the existing processing system, to simply switch over and sell their milk unpasteurized. Some are doing it, and finding they must significantly alter their entire approach to farming and milking. As just one example, most raw-milk consumers want their milk from grass-fed cows. For many dairies, this means setting up fields for pasture grazing, and abandoning the CAFO (confined animal feedlot operation) approach and its emphasis on grain feeding. It also means improving sanitation and safety procedures overall. And if the milk is to be labeled "organic," it means ensuring that all pasture hasn't been treated with pesticides for at least three years.

In addition, some big processors, in their contracts with dairies, require the dairies to provide the processors all their milk; private sales of raw milk are prohibited.

That isn't to say some dairies aren't making the transition, and making it successfully. The second-largest raw dairy in the country, The Family Cow in Pennsylvania, was a conventional dairy for many years, until 2005, when it consciously made the transition to being a raw milk dairy [9]. It took three years for the dairy to complete the transition to becoming an organic dairy. For consumers as well as farmers, though, such a transition poses challenges, as the dairy owners need to un-learn habits associated with mass producing milk, and learn new approaches for producing smaller batches of safe milk.

How big is the conventional dairy industry?

The American dairy industry is huge—estimated at about $125 billion in annual sales, according to several studies I have seen. This represents about 25% of the world dairy industry, which is estimated at nearly $500 billion.

What is its clout?

As noted, the dairy industry is an oligopoly. It is dominated by one corporate producer, Dean Foods, which controls from 35% to 90% of production, depending on the area of the country. This isn't well known to consumers because most of its milk is sold under other brands, like Garelick, Meadow Gold, Brown's Dairy, and Alta Deena. A handful of cooperatives like Organic Valley control much of the rest of production.

These producers have a huge amount of clout. They work with the FDA to set and adjust the rules of dairy production, and they have trade associations that lobby Congress on laws and regulations affecting the dairy industry.

How many people today drink raw milk?

The CDC sponsored a survey in 2007 and 2008 known as the Foodnet Survey [10]. Representatives of a research organization called people in ten states to ask them about which of a long list of foods they had eaten in the previous week. One of those foods was raw milk, and it turned out that an average of three per cent of respondents said they had been drinking raw milk. If you extrapolate that result to the entire country, it means about ten million people (out of 330 million) are raw milk drinkers.

This number was much higher than even the most ardent raw milk supporters had estimated—most of them estimated that perhaps one per cent of the population was regularly drinking raw milk.

Because of the increasing number of articles about raw milk, and the increasing number of state and federal legislative proposals to make raw milk more easily accessible to people, along with reports by raw milk producers of growing demand, it's assumed that raw milk's popularity has increased since that CDC study of 2007-2008.

How does raw milk fit into the growing interest in natural and organic food?

Raw milk has certainly become a symbol of the growing concern many people have about excessive food processing, since pasteurized milk is our first truly processed food. As noted, it is heated to more than 160 degrees, fractionated to remove much of its cream, and then spun at high speeds before it is packaged into plastic bottles and cartons. Even the cows that produce milk are raised in factory-like conditions, with idyllic pastures having long ago been replaced by huge sheds and corralled spaces, or feed lots, housing as many as 10,000 cows in a single facility.

Over the last 100 years, milk production has shifted from its agrarian roots dating back thousands of years into a mass-production model—the centerpiece of a $100-billion-plus industry. A big part of the lore around the transitioning of raw milk into a processed food was that extensive processing, overseen by government public health and agriculture experts, was essential to turn what had become a dangerous food into a safe food. Several generations of public health and medical professionals, including veterinarians, have been trained to view milk that way—as inherently unsafe unless it goes through the mandated processing.

The result was the creation of an edifice—a highly profitable industry controlled by a few major corporate structures, supported by large government agencies and medical associations—all arrayed in support of pasteurized milk and fiercely opposed to raw milk.

Confusing the matter even further is the reality that most of the milk produced by feedlot operations for pasteurization shouldn't ever be consumed unpasteurized. The cows are kept in such close, unsanitary conditions that significant amounts of their milk is tainted by pathogens, according to studies of milk intended for processing. The producers count on the heat of pasteurization to kill off any pathogens from their unsanitary practices and render the milk "safe."

Do raw milk proponents want to do away with pasteurized milk?

No one who advocates for raw milk is suggesting that the mass-produced milk suddenly be served unpasteurized. That would likely be a public health disaster, as noted in a few previous responses, simply because the raw milk produced by factory farms isn't reliably safe in its natural state. Knowing that their milk will be zapped gives producers of conventional milk "wiggle room" that producers of milk intended to be served raw don't have.

How do doctors and other health care providers feel about raw milk?

Organizations that represent physicians are fairly united in their opposition to raw milk. This includes the American Medical Association (AMA) and the American Academy of Pediatrics (AAP). The reason is that most health care professionals were taught during their professional training that raw milk is highly risky and that pasteurization was one of the great public health accomplishments of all time.

Moreover, it is important to appreciate that these professionals were trained at universities that have, in many cases, received significant funding from large food corporations that oppose raw milk.

But some physicians are beginning to question the near-universal medical professional opposition to raw milk. When members of the American Academy of Family Physicians introduced at a 2014 national Congress a recommendation to ban raw milk, several physicians spoke in opposition. The proposed ban recommendation was put off, and the matter referred to directors for further study.

And beneath the surface of the establishment opposition, there are a number of medical professionals who not only recommend raw milk, but actually sell it to their patients. A group of pediatricians in the San Francisco Bay area has long advised parents to serve raw milk to their children to improve their health. A physician in the New York City area sells raw milk to patients so they won't have to trek to farms to pick it up. A Massachusetts dentist with a large regional practice advocates for raw milk. And among alternative health care providers, like naturopaths and chiropractors, raw milk is extremely popular as a recommended health option. Osteopathic physician Joseph Mercola, whose

Mercola.com is one of the highest-traffic healthcare web sites [11] in the country, is an active proponent of raw milk.

What about raw milk cheese? I see that being sold in even large supermarkets. Is it as controversial as raw milk?

It has not been, primarily because the FDA, back in the late 1940s, created a rule for raw milk cheese production that has guided it practically to this day. The agency decreed that raw milk cheese should be aged 60 days before being offered for sale. The idea was to allow pathogens that might be present, time to die off.

While some cheese makers have complained that the approach makes it difficult to produce the soft fresh raw milk cheeses that the French are famous for, overall, the approach seems to have worked. There have been few illnesses from raw milk cheeses aged 60 days. (There have been illnesses from fresh cheeses, particularly queso fresco, a fresh cheese popular in Hispanic communities, and not legal under FDA rules.)

But like everything related to raw milk, even seemingly safe raw milk cheese has attracted controversy in recent years. The FDA has threatened to change the 60-day aging requirement, suggesting it might increase the minimum aging to longer than 60 days. (More on the risks associated with raw milk cheese in Chapter 6 on safety and risk.)

Chapter 3: Why the History of Raw Milk Matters So Much

Up until the 1800s, most people lived in rural settings, and simply drank the milk of their own goats and cows, or shared it with a few neighbors.

One of our best historical resources on the role of milk in mankind's early days is the Bible. It makes frequent references to milk, at least half a dozen, with a promise of the divine—as in Exodus, to bring the freed Israelites "into the land . . . which he swore to your fathers to give you, a land flowing with milk and honey." It was a respected and desired food, equal to wine as a symbol of celebration, as in the Song of Solomon: "I came to my garden, my sister, my bride, I gathered my myrrh with my spice, I ate my honeycomb with my honey, I drank my wine with my milk. Eat, friends, drink, and be drunk with love!"

Interestingly, there are no concerns expressed in the Bible over raw milk's safety.

But, of course, things changed.

I grew up learning from my high school history that lots of children died from drinking raw milk. Why did safety suddenly become a problem?

Raw milk safety problems first emerged in the mid-1800s, when huge numbers of people began moving from the country to the city as part of the Industrial Revolution. Over the next fifty years or so, millions of people moved to cities in the East and Midwest to get work in the vast new factories that were starting up, producing everything from textiles to shoes to nuts and bolts.

With the new city arrivals came their cows—after all, families wanted to continue drinking milk. Not surprisingly, raising cows in cities didn't work real well, especially when it was done by business people who knew little about animal husbandry and cared even less. They began keeping cows in areas of Brooklyn, Boston, and Chicago in what amounted to the first feedlots, and they were disgusting places. The cows were often fed the leftovers from distilleries and wound up malnourished, making their milk blue in color. Producers added chalk to make it look white. The men who milked them were often sick with tuberculosis and other diseases. There was little appreciation about the importance of sanitation and no understanding of how pathogens were passed from feces to the milk.

There were terrible outbreaks of typhoid fever, tuberculosis, diphtheria, and other diseases, resulting in thousands, including many children, being killed.

Were all these diseases traceable to bad raw milk?

There were no epidemiological studies or tests to pinpoint causes back then because so little was known about the role of pathogens in causing disease, let alone the overall importance of sanitation and worker health in keeping a lid on outbreaks. That being said, it's probably not fair to place the blame for all the many outbreaks of disease that occurred in American cities (as well as cities around the world) entirely on milk. Bad drinking water, tainted by human sewage, likely played a role, as did all the manure from horses that clogged city streets. But milk was associated with enough of the cases so that, by the early 1900s, officials in several of the cities ravaged by disease, beginning with Chicago and New York, began looking to pasteurization as a solution to the outbreaks.

Wasn't pasteurization developed initially by Louis Pasteur to extend the shelf life of wine?

Pasteurization is a process of heating food to kill bacteria, and extend shelf life. Yes, it was developed by Louis Pasteur, one of the most prominent scientists of the 1800s (originator of "the germ theory," under which germs are deemed responsible for much illness), to help combat spoilage during the transport of French wines. Ironically, French winemakers abandoned the process after several decades, concluding that the heating adversely affected taste.

But pasteurization as a food processing technique moved forward. A commercial pasteurizer was patented in Germany in 1893, and by 1900, a standard set of pasteurization conditions was first defined. Ironically, Pasteur himself had nothing to do with milk pasteurization. Others took his process and began applying it to milk. Today, standard milk pasteurization involves heating milk to 161 degrees for 15 seconds.

You previously made mention of fractionating and homogenization. Can you explain these?

It's important to appreciate that pasteurization is just one step in a multifaceted processing scheme. Before anything happens to mass-market milk, it is fractionated to obtain the different variations we are accustomed to seeing in the supermarket—skim, one-per-cent, two-per-cent, and "whole" milk. All these variations are produced via fractionating, whereby varying amounts of butterfat, in the form of cream, are pulled from the milk. "Skim" milk is just as the name suggests—essentially all the cream is removed, or "skimmed," from the milk. For the other types (like 1% or 2% milk), the butterfat is similarly all removed, and then the promised amount added back in. Even "whole" milk, which originally had four per cent or more butterfat, is sold with 3.25% butterfat in the U.S. (with slight variations in other countries).

The butterfat that processors remove is then used to produce butter, whipping cream, and ice cream, among other products. Once you appreciate the role of fractionating, you also appreciate that the processors love to sell as much skim and other low-fat milk as possible. Such milk sells for the same price as whole milk, but it has less of what many raw milk drinkers consider to be "the good stuff"—the cream that gives raw milk its special texture and taste. You also appreciate that the $4 or $5 per gallon retail price for milk isn't the entire revenue stream from a gallon of milk. The cream that has been removed generates additional revenue for those other dairy products.

In addition, nearly all milk that is pasteurized is also homogenized. This is a process developed in the 1930s of spinning the milk at high speeds and forcing it through filters to break up the fat globules so that the milk no longer separates, with the cream rising to the top. Because people used to value the cream at the top—some skimmed it off to put in their coffee or to make butter, or just enjoy separately—the processors had to "educate" people that homogenization was the more "modern" way of drinking milk, and non-homogenized milk was old fashioned. Homogenization allows milk to sit on the shelf for a few days, without all that cream at the top reminding people the milk has been sitting for a while.

Homogenization is thought by some raw milk aficionados to adversely affect the nutritional composition of the milk, making the fat less easily digestible, and less nutritious.

How well did pasteurization work when it was introduced in the early 1900s?

As outbreaks from raw milk persisted into the early 1900s, public health professionals in a number of big cities encouraged some milk producers to try using pasteurization. All involved were thrilled with the results. The first city to begin requiring pasteurization was Chicago, followed by New York, then Boston, Philadelphia, Milwaukee, and San Francisco. The benefits were seen almost immediately. As one example, the infant mortality rate for those less than one year of age fell from a rate of 160 deaths for every 1,000 births in 1906 to 90 in 1916.

Public health professionals were especially impressed by declines in tuberculosis. This was a particularly brutal disease, that often laid waste its victims over months, or even years.

In the view of the U.S. Centers for Disease Control (CDC), pasteurization was a huge success. "It led to dramatic reductions in the number of people getting sick from diseases that had previously been transmitted commonly by milk. Most public health professionals and health care providers consider pasteurization to be one of public health's most effective food safety interventions ever!"

If pasteurization was such a "miracle," why wasn't it required nationally?

The short answer to this question is that responsibility for food safety—cleanliness of restaurants, food retail stores, and farms--is mostly a state and local matter, regulated by state departments of agriculture and public health, as well as county and town public health boards. In recent years, the federal government has become more involved in raw milk, and food safety in general. In 1987, the U.S. Food and Drug Administration, on orders of a U.S. District judge, prohibited interstate shipment and sale of raw milk. In 2011, Congress enacted the Food Safety Modernization Act, which gave the federal government broad new powers over food producers of all kinds, including farms.

What is the longer answer?

Raw milk has a history as a nourishing, even healing, food. In the early 1900s, physicians often prescribed raw-milk-based diets to help people heal from diseases like tuberculosis and arthritis, and wrote a number of books advocating its medicinal benefits. The predecessor of the Mayo Clinic in Minnesota gave patients raw milk therapeutically, sometimes exclusively for several weeks at a time.

Interestingly, pasteurization only gained acceptance very gradually through the 1900s because much of the conventional medical wisdom of the day claimed health benefits for unpasteurized milk. Individuals with tuberculosis and other diseases sent to sanitariums were often put on diets consisting primarily of raw milk, and established physicians reported positive results in many cases. Prominent physicians helped establish and operate something called the Medical Milk Commission, which was designed to certify farms producing safe raw milk, out of New Jersey from the late 1800s up until the middle of the last century.

As a result of the medical community's support of raw milk, it took Chicago eight years to mandate full pasteurization in 1916. The haphazard adoption of pasteurization left many people still drinking raw milk early in the twentieth century; according to the U.S. Centers for Disease Control, by the mid-1930s, about one-fourth of all illnesses from food resulted from tainted raw milk.

It wasn't until 1947 that Michigan became the first state to require that all milk be pasteurized, essentially outlawing the sale of raw milk. Other states, like Ohio, Virginia, and Maryland followed suit. But while some twenty states wound up requiring pasteurized milk, and in effect banning the sale of raw milk, another thirty states continued to allow raw milk sales in one form or another—direct from the farm or via retail sales. (More on the regulations affecting the availability of raw milk, in Chapter 7.)

It seems as if the diseases that created all the problems in the late 1800s and early 1900s—like typhoid, diphtheria, and tuberculosis—are no longer with us. Why the continuing government concern about raw milk safety?

That is correct, those old-time deadly diseases are no longer with us, having been vanquished by a combination of improved sanitation practices (like sewers and water treatment) and vaccination...and a growing awareness among farmers producing raw milk, that great care must be taken to consistently produce safe raw milk. Moreover, agriculture and public health professionals have encouraged highly successful eradication programs for tuberculosis and brucellosis in cows, which continue to be mandated in many states.

The illnesses that can be transmitted via raw milk today are the same illnesses that can be transferred via any food—pathogens like *Salmonella*, *Campylobacter*, and *Listeria*, which mostly cause stomach upset for several days, and pass.

However, some of today's pathogens can lead to serious health problems. For example, *Listeria* can cause miscarriages in pregnant women and even death in the elderly and immune-compromised. And a pathogen known as *E. coli* O157:H7, which was only discovered in the early 1980s, can cause a very serious complication, known as hemolytic uremic syndrome (HUS). It shows up in fewer than 10% of *E. coli* O157:H7 cases, but when it does, it is very serious. Especially in children, HUS can lead to a temporary shutdown of the kidneys, and possible long-term kidney damage.

The question of raw milk risk is a subject I discuss in detail in Chapter 6.

What is the dairy industry's position today with regard to milk safety?

The dairy industry takes the position that pasteurized milk is the safest milk option, and that raw milk is an unsafe milk option. It argues that outbreaks of illness associated with raw milk raise questions about safety for all milk. The industry says it doesn't want problems with raw milk to denigrate from the entire dairy industry, and that's why it campaigns so hard against raw milk.

Chapter 4: How Risky Is Raw Milk, Really?

This may sound weird, but the first time I drank raw milk, back in 2006, I went to bed worried I might wake up deathly ill...or not wake up at all.

The issue of risk is the one that creates the most fear, and controversy, around raw milk. Public health authorities argue that raw milk is just too risky for most people, and particularly for children and individuals with compromised immune systems, like those undergoing chemotherapy. The CDC even has a web site [1] with interviews of individuals who got sick from raw milk, or whose children got sick.

Advocates of raw milk contend that the risks associated with raw milk have been overstated. They say there are risks associated with all foods, and that even pasteurized milk has made people seriously ill, and even killed a few.

Doesn't all milk that comes from the cow (or other animals) contain certain natural bacteria and cells?

Yes, all milk contains a variety of harmless bacteria, including lactic acid bacteria and coliforms. These are thought to come from the cow as well as from the environment and from dust and dirt in the environment, and even from manure.

Milk can also contain staphylococcus and streptococcus bacteria that cause mastitis infections in cows (an infection of the udder); these are generally harmless to people, though in sufficient quantities can cause stomach upset.

Milk also contains somatic cells, which are blood cells that fight infection, and occur naturally in milk.

Are these bacteria and cells good for us or potentially harmful?

As I indicated, these bacteria are generally harmless. There are two views of their relevance. Some raw milk advocates feel that these naturally occurring bacteria are just a few among many that are good for us, helping our bodies build general immunity and replenishing the microbiome (our bodies' overall community of bacteria and other micro-components).

However, high counts of any of these bacteria and cells can also be an indication of unsanitary conditions in the milking or storage of milk. Oftentimes, high bacterial counts in fresh milk lead to the milk "turning", or smelling badly, after just a few days. Milk with very low counts usually won't begin smelling badly for two or even three weeks. (Though such unpleasant smells don't mean the milk is rancid; rather, it is an indication of fermentation under way, which rarely makes people ill.)

Milk processors generally do a number of standard measurements—standard plate count (SPC), coliform count (CC), and somatic cell count (SCC)—before milk is pasteurized, to provide dairies with a gauge as to the cleanliness of their facilities and the health of their cows. Some processors pay financial premiums to dairies for meeting low-count standards.

What about raw milk producers—do they do these tests?

Some producers do these tests themselves. In the 30 states where raw milk can legally be sold from the farm or at retail, state departments of agriculture generally conduct these tests on a monthly or quarterly basis.

Do these bacteria and cells pose any danger?

Not in and of themselves. While milk is nearly 90% water, the rest is highly nutritive. But it is also an ideal medium for the rapid multiplication of any and all bacteria, especially at room temperatures and if it contains manure. Milk with high coliform and somatic cell counts is thought to be more at risk for harboring pathogens, since they are more likely to be present and to multiply in unsanitary conditions, and in unhealthy animals.

Isn't there data from the CDC or other official sources on illnesses and deaths from raw milk, to help us assess risk?

Amazingly, the CDC and FDA don't present data on reported illnesses from any food, including raw milk, on an annual basis, to allow trends to be graphed on a year-to-year basis. The only way to obtain data is to extract it yourself from something called the Foodborne Outbreak Online Database [2] maintained by the CDC.

When it comes to illnesses from raw milk, the CDC and FDA seem only to provide data in clumps, based on arbitrary groupings of, say five, eight, or fifteen years. As one example, this from a CDC FAQ: "From 1998 through 2011, 148 outbreaks due to consumption of raw milk or raw milk products were reported to CDC. These resulted in 2,384 illnesses, 284 hospitalizations, and 2 deaths."

Does anyone have the data?

I have gone through the tedious process of extracting annual data from the CDC database. When you examine CDC data over the last decade [3], you find that there are generally between 25 and 200 reported illnesses from raw milk each year. In 2008 there were 132, in 2011 there were 60. There is no long-term trend up or down (though from 2006-2010 the trend was steadily up, before the number of illnesses plummeted in 2011).

So what I did was take a typical recent year for both raw milk illnesses, and total foodborne illnesses as reported by the CDC. That way, we are comparing apples and apples.

What did you find?

What I found was as follows:

*In 2008, there were 23,000 total foodborne illnesses reported by the CDC.

*132 came from raw milk and raw milk cheese.

*Thus, slightly over one half of one per cent of the total reported illnesses was from raw milk.

That is it? No one else breaks it down this way?

There is a web site run by the prominent food safety lawyer, Bill Marler, known as realrawmilkfacts.com [4], which maintains data on illnesses from raw [5] and pasteurized [6] milk. It shows graphics on annual reported illnesses, from pasteurized milk and raw milk; it also provides a list of the actual outbreaks (type of facility, location) and illnesses from raw milk extracted from the CDC database I alluded to above.

Is there anything else we don't know about the data on raw milk illnesses?

Yes, we don't know how many of the illnesses attributed to raw milk come from "pre-pasteurized" milk—that milk intended for processing, not intended to be served raw. As one example, in 2011 a mom took some milk from the bulk tank of a conventional Wisconsin dairy that sells pre-pasteurized milk, to a school birthday party. Some 18 people got sick, most of them children, with *Campylobacter*. Food safety officials in Wisconsin essentially excused the farm owners for the "accident," since they didn't intend to publicly distribute unpasteurized milk.

However, those 18 illnesses were tallied in the CDC's databases as illnesses attributed to raw milk for 2011. So, of the 60 illnesses reported by the CDC in 2011, 30% came from pre-pasteurized milk....that we know about. Put another way, had those 18 not been included in the tally, there would have been only 42 illnesses attributed to raw milk.

Pretty much the same situation occurred in Wisconsin in 2014, when 38 high school students in the small town of Durand became sick, from raw milk brought in for a football team dinner by a commercial dairy farmer who sells his milk for pasteurization.

Are there other such situations that distort the data?

There almost certainly are. As another example, some

illnesses attributed to raw milk come from tainted queso fresco cheese—a soft Mexican cheese used to jazz up salads and enchiladas, and popular in the Hispanic community. Because it isn't aged 60 days as required by the FDA for cheese, and is traditionally made from pre-pasteurized milk (milk intended for pasteurization), it is often produced for local communities by home food producers...in bathtubs, of all places (hence its nickname, "bathtub cheese.")

So you are saying this has inflated the data on raw milk illnesses?

Yes, these sorts of tabulation glitches appear to have inflated illnesses, and even deaths, from raw milk. The FDA and CDC will often say (as quoted in an answer above) that two people have died from tainted raw milk over the last 20 years. It turns out those two died from bad queso fresco cheese. Raw milk advocates complain that using those deaths to denigrate raw milk is highly misleading.

There is also the matter of something scientists refer to as "diagnostic bias" involved here—that cases attributed to raw milk consumption are so much easier to identify than cases attributed to other food commodities that are frequently consumed by many people. The CDC has stated that only one in every 38 cases of foodborne illness can be traced back to its source. Raw milk is easier to zero in on as a possible cause of illness because it is much less frequently consumed compared to many other foods.

Have the CDC and FDA shown any interest in adjusting or fixing the data?

Quite the contrary. The CDC and FDA are focused on highlighting as many illnesses as they can possibly associate with raw milk, and then sensationalizing the data. As one example, the CDC in 2012 conducted an analysis claiming to the media that raw milk is 150 times more dangerous than pasteurized milk [7]. What the agency didn't clarify sufficiently for media people not familiar with the complexity associated with data on foodborne illnesses is that its data, based as it was on outbreaks, was much different than it would have been had the agency been consistent with other reports, and focused on actual illnesses.

Why is that a problem?

An outbreak is two or more illnesses. When there is an outbreak from raw milk, it generally involves just a few people, less than fifty. But when there is an outbreak from pasteurized milk, it can, and has, involved many thousands of people, because pasteurized milk is so much more widely consumed. For example, a 1987 outbreak of salmonellosis tied to pasteurized milk sickened as many as 197,000 people, according to a report in the *Journal of the American Medical Association*. And a 1994 salmonellosis outbreak sickened 224,000 people, and was eventually traced to tainted pasteurized-milk ice cream.

So in the CDC tabulations, those 400,000-plus illnesses only counted for two outbreaks. It would take hundreds and hundreds of raw milk outbreaks over many years to ever even begin to approach that number of illnesses.

It also seems as if the news media play up raw milk's dangers more than its potential benefits. Is this correct?

I haven't done a scientific survey of the many articles that have been written about raw milk since 2006, but there have been dozens, and I would venture that nearly all of them include a strong warning from the CDC and/or the FDA about raw milk's safety. The warnings strongly advise readers to completely avoid raw milk because it can cause them to become seriously ill, or even die.

The publications also quote public health and medical experts ridiculing stories of people who have gained relief from conditions like allergies as "anecdotal," saying no evidence exists that raw milk confers health benefits on drinkers.

Even publications that have a liberal, anti-establishment orientation, like *Mother Jones* [8] and *Slate* [9], have come out with harshly anti-raw-milk articles, in significant measure because of the writers' perception that raw milk advocates are political extremists unconcerned with food safety.

If huge institutions like the mainstream media, medical establishment, and dairy industry are so down on raw milk, how come it seems to be increasing in popularity, and pasteurized milk decreasing in popularity?

That is the $64,000 question, as they say. Why would intelligent people who care about their families' safety seem to ignore the many warnings by those at the top of the medical and public health establishments?

The answer, in my judgment (and as suggested in Chapter

2), is that increasing numbers of people are highly skeptical of advice and conclusions from places like the FDA, CDC and medical sources, including their own doctors. There have been so many reports about serious and unexpected side effects from prescription drugs, along with concerns about skyrocketing rates of auto-immune disorders like asthma and allergies, that substantial numbers of people have become highly cynical about the established health care system. As a result, people are increasingly looking for natural alternatives, and raw milk appears to be one way to satisfy that concern.

Wouldn't it be logical to expect health-care professionals to become more sensitive to the growing number of people feeding their families' raw milk?

I am not sure many of these professionals are aware of just how extensive the shift to raw milk has become. That may be because their patients don't talk about their shifts. I know of individuals who simply don't tell their doctors about their or their children's raw milk habits, out of fear the parents may be cited for being less than adequate parents.

Aren't you being a tad paranoid?

Not necessarily. In Maine, a physician in 2013 reported to family services a mother who had told him about how pleased she was with her infant son's improved health after being fed an infant formula based on raw goat milk. The state backed off after supporters of the mother banded together and complained to politicians and also organized demonstrations outside the doctor's office.

How do the public health authorities justify their argument about raw milk's riskiness?

I have heard them justify their position in several ways:

1. A common argument has to do with a cow's anatomy—the position of the cow's teats near the cow's anus can easily cause manure to get into the milk. I've heard a state agriculture inspector advise that raw milk should be consumed the same day it is produced, suggesting that waiting more than a day increases the risk that the milk will be overrun by dangerous bacteria.

2. They also argue that raw milk's inherent riskiness means you never know for sure when illness might turn up. Here is one statement from the CDC [10] on one of its web sites: "The presence of germs in raw milk is unpredictable. The number of disease-causing germs in the raw milk may be too low to make a person sick for a long time, and later high enough to make the same person seriously ill. For some people, drinking contaminated raw milk just once could make them really sick."

3. Public health professionals also point to cases in which children have become seriously ill from raw milk—there have been a handful of instances in which children contracted hemolytic uremic syndrome (HUS), a side effect for up to ten per cent of children who are sickened with the pathogen E.coli 0157:H7 (regardless of whether they contract the pathogen via raw milk or any other food). Children with HUS usually lose kidney function for some days, requiring dialysis while the kidneys recover.

In some of these cases, photos of children on dialysis have circulated on social media, creating a terrifying image for parents.

Do public health professionals feel the problems of illness from raw milk can be solved via improved safety measures by raw milk dairies?

That question points up an issue of increased contention within the public health community. There are many in the field of public health, including those setting policy at the FDA and CDC, who argue that raw milk is "inherently unsafe." In other words, there is no way, in their view, that any sort of safety measures can counter the inherent dangers.

Then, there is a small but growing minority within the public health community—mostly coming from individuals at universities and local departments of public health and agriculture as well as veterinarians—who feel that raw milk's dangers can be significantly countered with improved safety measures. I discuss a number of these safety measures in Chapter 8 on finding the safest raw milk.

I don't see any way of reconciling these two views. If you believe raw milk is inherently unsafe—in other words, it cannot be produced safely no matter what precautions dairies take—then there is no need for further discussion. You want to see raw milk banned, period, end of discussion.

Aren't there some straightforward ways to quantify the risk?

This is a logical question. To truly assess risk, we should know whether the risk of getting sick from raw milk is one in 100, one in 1,000, or one in a million. What about the risk of dying? Surely there must be a straightforward answer, given how long milk has been around, and how intensively the question of raw milk has been debated over the decades.

Unfortunately, like most questions involving raw milk, the answer seems to vary according to the person's views, pro or con. That is because the data is incomplete. Most notably, we don't have ongoing data about raw milk consumption that could help quantify risk on a per-serving basis. And we don't have comparative data on illnesses from different foods.

Still, even in this data vacuum, a number of experts have attempted to provide risk assessments. According to Ted Beals, a retired pathologist and professor at the University of Michigan, and a raw milk proponent, you have a greater chance of getting injured in an auto accident on the way to the farm than you have of getting sick from the raw milk you actually buy.

But CDC researchers say raw milk is a terrible danger [11]: "It is important to note that a substantial proportion of the raw-milk-associated disease burden falls on children; among the 104 outbreaks from 1998-2011 with information on the patients' ages available, 82% involved at least one person younger than 20 years old." The CDC didn't say how this percentage compares to other foods.

So which is it? As remote as being struck by lightning, or a serious risk of children becoming sick?

The short answer is we don't know. Part of the reason we don't know is that our public health establishment, which monitors food-borne illness, hasn't been willing to do the kind of research necessary to provide a serious risk analysis and comparison to other foods.

What is your opinion?

I happen to not agree with either assessment. I know that a number of children have become seriously ill from raw milk, which I discuss in more detail in Chapter 5 on food safety. The nonprofit organization, Center for Science and the Public Interest, says that 70% of all illnesses from dairy result from raw milk, which is a high percentage, considering that likely three per cent of the population or less is drinking raw milk.

I also know that hundreds of thousands of people are drinking raw milk each day, without any hint of illness. In Massachusetts, where I live, and where raw milk is sold directly from approximately 25 licensed dairies to consumers, there hasn't been an illness reported from a licensed raw dairy in the state since it began licensing dairies in the 1990s. In surrounding states, like New Hampshire and Maine, the situation is similar. Vermont had a handful of illnesses in 2010, according to state regulators, but from the description they provided during legislative hearings seeking approval of new regulations to broaden raw milk distribution, it seems as if most or all of the illnesses came from dairies that primarily sell raw milk for pasteurization, and not from dairies that are regulated to sell it raw.

One other thing: In my experience, a few dairies with identifiable problems have been responsible for the most serious illnesses. Or, put another way, there are hundreds of small dairies selling raw milk that have been doing it for years without a single illness.

But there have been some very serious illnesses from raw milk, right?

Yes, there have, and these should not only be acknowledged but analyzed so that lessons can be learned to avoid problems in the future.

While the most serious outbreaks, those involving E.coli 0157:H7, have been scattered around the country, the preponderance of those cases since 2005 have been associated with unregulated dairies, as opposed to dairies that obtain state permits.

A few of the illnesses have been given repeated publicity, which has magnified their publicity effect. For example, after seven-year-old Chris Martin became seriously ill in 2006, most likely from tainted milk from a California regulated dairy, his mother, Mary McGonigle-Martin, became a passionate spokesperson against the risks of raw milk, testifying at several state legislative hearings on raw milk against legislation that would liberalize its availability, and being quoted in a dozen or more articles about raw milk.

How is it that raw milk can be sold from unregulated dairies?

A number of states allow raw milk sales from the farm, but don't inspect, test, or otherwise regulate the dairies. I provide more detail about these situations in Chapters 7 and 8, on locating raw milk and buying the safest raw milk.

Have there been any concerns expressed about pasteurized milk's inherent safety?

Interestingly, a 2014 analysis [12] by half a dozen scientists raised questions about whether increasing pasteurization temperatures, as a possible way to protect against bioterror infiltration of the milk supply, could make milk more susceptible to contamination from pathogenic *Listeria*. The title of the analysis made the point: "Responding to bioterror concerns by increasing milk pasteurization temperature would increase estimated annual deaths from listeriosis." Keep in mind this was a theoretical analysis based on mathematical modeling and such—similar in style to studies that have been used to criticize raw milk and raw milk cheese as especially dangerous--but the scientists concluded, "Conservative estimates of the effect of pasteurizing all fluid milk at 82°C rather than 72°C are that annual listeriosis deaths from consumption of this milk would increase from 18 to 670, a 38-fold increase..." That is a pretty significant increase, an "unintended consequence," as the authors put it, of the seemingly logical step of heating milk more intensively as a way to kill off bacteria.

Doesn't the fact that there were more illnesses and deaths from pasteurized milk products than raw milk products suggest the pasteurized stuff is more dangerous?

Probably not. Pasteurized milk is much more widely consumed than raw milk. If they were equally risky for foodborne illness, there would be many more illnesses from pasteurized milk.

Why don't illnesses and deaths from pasteurized dairy get more media attention? It seems like I never hear about people getting sick from pasteurized milk?

As I said in answer to the previous two questions, there are proportionately fewer people getting sick from pasteurized milk than raw milk. That being said, though, the media rarely mention when a pasteurized-milk outbreak does occur, that pasteurized milk was the culprit, though they make a huge deal out if illnesses attributed to raw milk. That is because reports on the illnesses from the CDC and FDA usually ignore the presence of pasteurized milk when they write up their reports.

In a 2014 blog post [13], I analyzed two government reports examining outbreaks from pasteurized cheese in 2013 that had hospitalized 13 and killed two people. Neither made mention of the fact the cheese was from pasteurized milk, and glossed over the fact that at least three infants were among those sickened.

One exception came when three people died and one pregnant woman miscarried in 2007, the fact that pasteurized milk was the culprit did get wide publicity. Apparently, cleaning equipment helped spread *Listeria* to flavorings added after pasteurization at a commercial dairy in Massachusetts, leading to the deaths.

Are you suggesting there is a double standard in the media and government reporting on sicknesses from raw and pasteurized milk?

Yes, that is exactly what I am suggesting.

How can it be that experts with advanced degrees can come to such widely varying interpretations of risk?

The answer to that question requires that we understand something about the availability of data about food-borne illnesses. Such data is collected and presented by the CDC. Because the CDC is so intensely opposed to raw milk, it always seems to present data about such milk in as negative a way as it can.

As just one example, the CDC never presents data about raw milk in an annualized, trend-based format. Rather, it is always presented as a total over a number of years. Moreover, there's never any comparison to previous periods, plus it's nearly always different, from report to report.

So, a 2014 *Washington Post* article [14], presented the data this way: "The agency reported that 796 people in 24 states had become sick after consuming raw milk between 2006 and 2011, the latest years for which complete data are available."

A 2014 Fox News report [15] stated it this way: "According to the CDC, there were 2,384 illnesses, 284 hospitalizations and two deaths attributed to raw milk or raw milk products from 1998 through 2011."

Why is this a problem?

For two reasons. First, the presentation of seemingly large numbers, in isolation, obscures the reality that all foods make people sick. So, pick a food, and you will obtain similarly large sounding numbers over a period of five or ten years.

Second, because the numbers aren't annualized, people

can't get a sense of their context or meaning. Using the examples above, the numbers in the Washington Post article work out to an average of 132 illnesses per year over the six-year period cited. That number is out of a total of about 15,000 food-borne illnesses per year, or less than one per cent of the total.

The numbers in the Fox News report work out to an average of 170 per year over the 14 years cited. Does that mean the average went down during the more recent years, which the Washington Post article used? I don't know for sure, but my guess is that the Washington Post numbers were limited to "raw milk," while the Fox News report included data on "raw milk or raw milk products," which includes cheese, ice cream, and others.

If we're just talking numbers, why does anyone care?

Because the numbers are presented for "shock value"--so as to look much larger than they would if they were broken down on an annual basis. The reason that becomes problematic is that the CDC uses the data heavily for political purposes, to try to highlight raw milk's inherent danger.

If the data isn't as negative toward raw milk as you suggest, why can't journalists or other individuals simply get the more positive data?

Unfortunately, the data are difficult to access, or just not available. The raw data, as it were, is all in a not-easy-to-locate or use CDC web site [16]. This is the data that tells us we have about 15,000 reported illnesses from food each year.

And the data itself is nearly inaccessible, unless you have huge amounts of time.

How so?

Let's say you want to determine all the illnesses from a particular food—raw milk, pasteurized milk, chicken, ground beef, peanut butter—between 1998 and 2011, which is the reporting period available. You have to go through 787 pages of data [17], and manually locate the "food vehicle" under one column and "total ill" under another. But even then, your findings will likely be incomplete, since the "food vehicle" isn't always identified. And the listings are often imprecise. Raw dairy illnesses can be identified as "Milk, raw," "RAW MILK," "Goat milk, raw," "Cheese, unpasteurized," "Whole milk, unpasteurized," "Queso fresco," with no pasteurization status listed, and so on and so forth. The reason for these varying descriptors is that there is no drop-down standardized menu for the states, which supply the data to the CDC, to fill in.

This is the situation for any food people might be researching--you either have to do many hours of tedious work yourself, or look to someone else to do it for you. The CDC, of course, has huge manpower available to search out the data it wants to highlight, and quite often that data has to do with raw milk.

Are there no other data options?

There is one other data source for food-borne illnesses I am aware of-- a database [18] compiled by the Center for Science and the Public Interest, a nonprofit organization. Here, you can search by food, pathogen, or state, between 1990 and 2011. (But you can't search on two at a time; thus you can search out all the milk illnesses its database contains, but I couldn't find a way to then isolate by state or year.)Still, this is more accessible than the CDC database.

Where does CSPI obtain its data?

It says it "has tracked foodborne illness outbreaks -- events where two or more people become ill from eating the same food -- since 1997." In another place, it says it has data going back to 1990.

How closely does the data at CDC compare with that at CSPI?

Your guess is as good as mine. To find out for sure, you'd need to manually compare the two databases since they are set up according to different criteria.

My sense is that the two are fairly similar, since the CSPI reported [19] in 2013 that food borne illnesses had declined about 40% between 2000 and 2010—similar to reports from the CDC.

What about the estimates the media frequently publish, that there are 48 million cases of food-borne illness each year?

Those are estimated food-borne illness statistics. The CDC in effect says the real-life data it collects from state departments of public health is so unrepresentative of reality that it must resort to "estimates" to provide what it considers to be a true sense of how many illnesses there are. Lo and behold, those numbers [20] are huge, thousands of times the actual reported illnesses; 48 million illnesses (versus 15,000 reported illnesses) and 3,000 deaths (versus about 15 reported deaths) each year.

Within those estimates, the CDC provides approximations of which pathogens are causing how many illnesses...but nothing on which foods it estimates to be causing how many illnesses.

Why are there such huge discrepancies and inconsistencies?

No one knows for sure, but my sense is this is both a make-work issue as well as a control issue. So long as ordinary people can't easily access and compare data, we are dependent on the CDC scientists and academics—all of whom have lots of time and lots of (our) money—to ferret out the data for us.

When the CDC in 2010 lowered its estimates of annual food-borne illnesses from a mammoth 76 million to just a huge 48 million, some academics were concerned that the "mantra" of a food safety crisis was being undercut. Marion Nestle, a prominent food safety professor at New York University, bemoaned [21] the timing of the reduced number because it came just as the Food Safety Modernization Act was being debated in Washington. "It would be painfully ironic if CDC's 'better' numbers undercut enactment of the food safety bill," she wrote. (It eventually passed Congress and was signed into law by President Obama.)

So long as food-safety data remain inconsistent and incomplete, and subject to propaganda application by politicized bureaucrats and scientists, it doesn't have the credibility it should have. And thus, it becomes subject to ongoing criticism that don't help set realistic food safety priorities.

Chapter 5: What Are the Health Benefits of Raw Milk?

It is time to move from the anxiety-provoking side of raw milk to its inspiring side. One of the big reasons people are willing to assume the risks associated with raw milk is that they have read about or experienced health benefits from its consumption.

I have come across dozens of stories from people who say raw milk finally ended years of suffering from Crohn's, or enabled them at long last to be able to drink milk without the gas and other stomach upset they had with pasteurized milk. And mothers who say it was only raw milk, coming after use of various prescription drugs, including dangerous steroids, that finally pacified their young children's terrible bouts with eczema. Raw milk has also been the subject of impressive research out of Europe suggesting it can help counter asthma and allergies.

Wasn't there a time when the medical community actually supported raw milk as healthy, and even as a key therapeutic component in fighting serious diseases?

Ironically, during the early 1900s, when raw milk was being blamed for large-scale disease outbreaks occurring in American cities, the nation's medical community was very supportive of raw milk. A Connecticut naturopath (and author of the book, The Untold Story of Milk), Ron Schmid, writes this about physician attitudes [1]:

"Many people today find it surprising that support of raw milk among physicians was widespread in the first half of the twentieth century. The use of raw milk as a treatment of chronic disease has a rich and well-documented history.

In 1929, J. E. Crewe, MD, one of the founders of the Mayo Foundation, the forerunner of the Mayo Clinic in Rochester, Minnesota, published an article entitled "Raw Milk Cures Many Diseases." Here are excerpts from Dr. Crewe's account of his experience with raw milk:

" 'For fifteen years the writer has employed the certified milk treatment in various diseases and during the past ten he had a small sanitarium devoted principally to this treatment. The results obtained in various types of disease have been so uniformly excellent that one's conception of disease and its alleviation is necessarily changed.' "

Was there research to support these views?

According to Ron Schmid, there were a number of supportive studies [2]. He says that "from the earliest days of pasteurization, scientists demonstrated that heat treatment had a profound effect on the health-giving properties of milk. A loss of nutrients other than vitamin C was demonstrated in subsequent studies. One article, 'The effect of heat on the solubility of the calcium and phosphorus compounds in milk,' was published in 1925 in the *Journal of Biological Chemistry*. The author's conclusion was unequivocal: 'There is a loss in the soluble calcium and phosphorus contents of the milk due to heat and the amount of the loss depends upon the temperature to which the milk has been heated.' Other studies showed that pasteurization caused the loss of significant percentages of many of the B vitamins and nearly all of the enzymes in milk.

"Further compelling evidence of the superiority of raw milk appeared in *The Lancet* in 1937, in a report on the work of the medical officer to a group of orphanages. The physician gave pasteurized milk for five years to one group of 750 boys, while giving raw milk to another group of 750. All other conditions were alike except for this one item. During that period, 14 cases of tuberculosis occurred in the boys fed pasteurized milk, while only one occurred in those fed raw milk."

How come I don't hear today about research on raw milk's health benefits?

Since about 1950, when many states like Ohio and Michigan began passing laws requiring pasteurization, there has been little research done in the U.S. on raw milk's health benefits.

Why is that?

America's health and agriculture establishments, including the FDA, the CDC, National Institutes of Health, and agricultural colleges, have pretty much avoided the subject. I assume it has to do with the growing economic influence of the big dairy processing companies and cooperatives. They have consistently denigrated raw milk via negative media articles and lobbying efforts so as to get pasteurization laws passed, so there has for decades now been little appetite in the scientific community to counter the prevailing official attitudes and seek to do such research.

What do the CDC and FDA say about possible health benefits attributed to raw milk by Ron Schmid?

The CDC and FDA are adamant in their view that raw milk confers no special health benefits. They use this argument to advise people to drink pasteurized milk. The inference is that if raw and pasteurized milk confer the same health benefits, then why take any risk of getting sick from pathogens that might be present in raw milk?

Surely there has been nutritional analysis of pasteurized and raw milk. What do these comparisons show?

Like so many aspects of this subject, the answer to this question is more nuanced than the medical establishment often suggests. It comes down to how you define "nutrition." It's important to appreciate that nutrition can be assessed on two distinct levels.

First, there are the "standard label" nutrients—the fats, vitamins, minerals, sugars, and cholesterol levels that are identified on the label, as required by our food laws. In this dimension, the differences don't seem huge.

According to the anti-raw-milk site, Real Raw Milk Facts (RRMF) [3], "A comparison of the nutritional labels from a bottle of commercial raw whole milk and a bottle of organic, non-fortified pasteurized whole milk shows that there is little nutritional difference between the two milks--both raw and pasteurized milk contain similar key nutrients (which is also why bacteria grow well in either one). All milk is rich in proteins, carbohydrates, calcium and other nutrients. There are some enzymes that are destroyed by heat, but the enzymes in raw animal milk are not known to be important in human health."

How do we know the enzymes in raw animal milk aren't important in human health?

We don't really know. RRMF acknowledges that enzymes are damaged by heat. But when it says these enzymes "are not known to be important..." it is really saying there hasn't been scientific study of whether raw milk's enzymes are important enough to affect human health.

Is there evidence that the heat of pasteurization degrades milk's basic nutritional value?

According to Real Raw Milk Facts [4], no. "Milk is no different than other foods that we commonly cook. For example, cooked spinach or other fruits and vegetables and meats/ poultry/seafood are still full of nutrients even after heating."

You said there are two ways of assessing the nutritional benefits of raw milk. What is the second way?

Besides the vitamins, minerals, fat content, and cholesterol measured for required nutrition labels on milk sold in stores and supermarkets, there are other components that don't generally get recognized by American regulatory and public health authorities as counting for anything special. But some nutrition and medical experts say these other components should be measured, because they are what make raw milk significantly different from, and healthier than, pasteurized milk. These experts say it's important to consider such matters as the nature of the proteins and the composition of the fat, for example.

Has there been any official recognition of this second, more integrated, approach as applied to raw milk?

As it turns out, a panel of health and agriculture experts in Michigan examined the nutritional aspects of raw milk based on this more integrated approach. A group of 13 individuals — made up of farmers, academicians, healthcare professionals and regulatory officials — took six years to issue their 90-page report [5], in 2013, which was endorsed by the Michigan Department of Agriculture & Rural Development. The report has an unsexy title—"Report of Michigan Fresh Unprocessed Whole Milk Workgroup"—but its conclusions are provocative.

The report departs from the FDA's usual reasoning by suggesting that raw milk is more nutritious than pasteurized milk. "Milk fresh from the cow is a complete, living, functional food," with "immune system enhancers" that include enzymes, "cellular elements," prebiotics, special proteins and trace minerals beneficial to people.

Equally important, the report concluded that heat causes milk to lose nutritional benefits. "Proteins are incrementally denatured by heat" of pasteurization, the report noted. And fat, "of all the milk constituents ... is the most drastically altered by the combination of pasteurization and homogenization."

Does this have anything to do with the notion of the human "microbiome" we read about in the media?

It has a lot to do with the microbiome. The microbiome is the collection of complex communities of microbes –the trillions of bacteria, enzymes, and other microbes that inhabit our stomachs, intestines, noses, mouths, and other organs and orifices and seem to have a lot to do with not just digestion, but with immune function as well.

So as the Michigan report suggested, it's likely not just the enzymes or the "good" bacteria or the special proteins that allow raw milk to provide its health-giving benefits, but rather all its components working in synch.

Wouldn't such a holistic view seem to put to rest the idea that somehow the key nutritional parts of raw milk, like the special enzymes or proteins, can be "packaged" into some kind of pill form to avoid the safety concerns around raw milk?

I have heard public health people speculate about the possibility of somehow extracting the special proteins or enzymes or bacteria that make raw milk especially healthful, but I suspect it is more complicated than simply pulling one or another component out and packaging it.

One of the first efforts to probe the possibilities came in late 2014, when a group of scientists at the University of California, Davis, received a $6.9 million research grant [6] from the National Institutes of Health and the National Cancer Institute to focus "on a group of naturally occurring milk compounds called 'glycans,' " and how they "interact with beneficial bacteria in the infant gut to ease digestion, prevent inflammation and even fight cancer."

What about a new processing approach that eliminated pathogens, but didn't damage the proteins, enzymes, and good bacteria of raw milk like the heat of pasteurization does?

The dairy industry's operatives have long speculated about this, such as via ultraviolet treatment (as is used to pasteurize apple cider) or high pressure processing (HPP, which is used to process some raw vegetable juices). For example, in a report [7] by a dairy industry publication, Dairy Reporter, on research indicating that raw milk reduces infections in infants, the publication quoted a researcher: "The industry may come up with some way to treat raw milk without heat and without destroying the biologically active ingredients. That would be our wish to the dairy industry." But as of now, it appears to be no more than that: a wish, with no substance.

Is milk that is low-temperature pasteurized and non-homogenized a good substitute for raw milk?

The Weston A. Price Foundation, which advocates raw milk, appreciates that not everyone wants or can access raw milk. While it says raw milk is best, its annual printed guide for members on food suggestions says that full-fat pasteurized, non-homogenized, milk is "good" as an alternative.

But some purists disagree. One prominent food blogger, known as The Healthy Home Economist, contends [8], based on the microscopic structure visible in raw and pasteurized milk, that "even low temp pasteurization with no homogenization is a very damaging process!"

Is there more recent scientific evidence indicating that raw milk confers health benefits?

There have been about half a dozen studies since 2000 suggesting strongly that children who regularly drink raw milk have a significantly lower incidence of allergies and asthma than children who drink pasteurized milk.

The studies are mostly out of Europe, which is a reflection of the greater openness there to raw dairy than the U.S.

Do any of the studies stand out as most convincing?

One of the studies, known as the PARSIFAL study [9], and published in 2006, is convincing because of its scale-- it involved about 15,000 European children ages 5-13. According to the authors, "Our results indicated that the consumption of farm milk may offer protection against asthma and allergy."

Another of the studies, known as the GABRIELA study [10] and published in 2011, examined more than 8,000 children, and concluded, "Reported raw milk consumption was inversely associated to asthma, atopy (allergies) and hay fever, independent of other farm exposures...Boiled farm milk did not show a protective effect."

Even though none of the more than 20,000 children involved in the European studies was reported to have become ill from raw milk, the authors of the studies concluded they couldn't advocate consumption of raw milk because it has been associated with illness in the past.

And in 2014, the *Journal of Allergy and Clinical Immunology* published a study [11] by 20 European medical researchers in which the title seemed to say it all: "Consumption of unprocessed cow's milk protects infants from common respiratory infections." Based on a study of 983 infants, the study said that unpasteurized milk "reduced the risk of manifest respiratory infections and fever by about 30%."

What was it about raw milk that protected against these auto-immune disorders?

The scientists evaluating the results couldn't say for sure what raw milk did, and the authors of the PARSIFAL study didn't even try to hone in on the specifics. But the GABRIELA study authors did try to make determinations about which specific aspects of raw milk were so helpful. Significantly, they ruled out two raw milk traits that advocates like to associate with its health-improving qualities: "Total viable bacterial counts and total fat content of milk were not significantly related to asthma or atopy," the study concluded.

Instead, they speculated that one of several proteins, known as the whey protein, which was likely damaged by the heat of pasteurization, was key: "The findings suggest that the protective effect of raw milk consumption on asthma might be associated with the whey protein fraction of milk." Further clouding the subject, they limited their conclusion about the whey protein to asthma, since they didn't find the same correlations with allergies.

How do American public health officials explain these European studies?

For a good while, they simply ignored the studies. Then, the FDA's dairy chief, John Sheehan, in testimony he offered in 2013 against state raw milk legislation in Maine and California, began acknowledging the PARSIFAL study, and criticizing it because it wasn't always clear whether some European families boiled their "farm" milk, calling into question the comparisons of health benefits between raw and pasteurized milk.

But what about the GABRIELA study? That made a clear delineation in its research between raw and pasteurized milk.

American regulators have mostly waved off that more compelling study. The CDC in a series of questions and answers on its web site about raw milk poses a question [12] that suggests its awareness of the European research:

"Does drinking raw milk prevent or cure any diseases, such as asthma, allergies, heart disease, or cancer?

"No. There are no health benefits from drinking raw milk that cannot be obtained from drinking pasteurized milk that is free of disease-causing bacteria. The process of pasteurization of milk has never been found to be the cause of chronic diseases, allergies, or developmental or behavioral problems."

In late 2014, the FDA provided a more specific rebuke to the Gabriela study. In a written response [13] denying a petition by raw dairy owner Mark McAfee to ease the FDA's ban on interstate raw milk sales and shipments, the agency took issue with the study's significance. Said the FDA: "The

(GABRIELA study) authors state that they found that raw milk consumption was inversely associated to asthma independent of other farm exposures. However, the study did not control for other factors (e.g., family history of allergies, breastfeeding history) that may be relevant for allergic disease development."

The FDA also disagreed with the study's speculation that the whey protein might be key in providing protection. And it pointed to the study authors' stated concerns about raw milk safety as evidence the "authors do not believe that their research supports recommending consumption of raw milk…"

Are there any exceptions among the American scientific community?

Interestingly, there has been one quite notable exception, and it came to light on prime-time television. In a 2014 Public Broadcasting System (PBS) documentary segment on raw milk [14], a professor of food science and technology at the University of California, Davis, Bruce German, made a startling declaration based on the European studies: Raw milk, he said, "seems to have properties that confer an immunological benefit. The children who are consuming raw milk have dramatically fewer allergies…We have this protection from allergies and we don't know how it happens."

How about elsewhere in the world?

Internationally, the European research is attracting notice. A 2011 analysis of 40 studies [15] of pasteurized and raw milk, by Canadian public health researchers, published in the *Journal of Food Protection*, finally acknowledged in an "official" analysis, very tentatively, the possibility that raw milk "may have a protective association with allergy development... although this relationship may be potentially confounded by other farming-related factors."

And a 2014 assessment by New Zealand regulators [16] (as part of a reassessment by that government oriented toward easing restrictions) made a similar tentative acknowledgment of raw milk's possible health benefits: "There is no conclusive evidence to show that raw milk helps protect against serious disease. There are a few studies that suggest that drinking raw milk at an early age, along with other factors, may help reduce the risk of developing asthma, hay fever, or eczema but the science is not conclusive...."

Those seem tentative. Has there been anything more?

Yes, in 2012, a year after the Canadian study was published, an editor with the highly regarded international scientific publication, Nature, came out with a detailed analysis of the GABRIELA study. The editor, Anna Petherick, writing in a scientific newsletter [17] put out by the University of California, Davis, speculated in an article that pasteurization might "destroy complex proteins and other components that could bolster human health."

What was her evidence?

She was taken by the GABRIELA study, begun in 2005 and led by a scientist at University Children's Hospital in Munich, of 8,000 children in Austria, Germany, and

Switzerland. "Some lived in quaint villages and typically drank supermarket milk," said Petherick. "Others lived on farms and often drank raw milk. The researchers gathered samples of milk from family fridges across the Alps and gave them to their colleagues for blind testing of the fat content, whey proteins, and bacterial count. GABRIELA found substantive evidence that raw milk-consuming farm kids were much less likely to develop allergies including asthma and dermatitis during childhood."

Did Petherick speculate on what components of the raw milk might have provided the protection from asthma and other allergies?

Yes, she explained it this way: "The study reports that a category of components in raw milk affords much of this protection. Unlike the better-known casein proteins that compose about four-fifths of the protein content of cow's milk, and which are hard to denature with heat, the activities of most whey proteins (making up about one-fifth) are substantially reduced by high heat treatment. Three whey proteins appear particularly important in stopping farm children from getting allergies: a-lactalbumin, b-lactoglobulin, and another called BSA. The more of these whey proteins found in the Alpine milk, the stronger its preventative properties for asthma."

What about the suggestion by the Canadian researchers that the benefits experienced by raw milk drinkers were mostly a result of living in a farm environment?

According to Petherick, the GABRIELA researchers made

an allowance for those factors. "The study did many things well: it monitored a huge cohort of kids, and it corrected for important confounding factors – for example, the tendency for children with more older siblings to have fewer allergies and for farming families to be bigger. It also double-checked the conclusions by considering farm kids who drank milk boiled at home. (The results were broadly the same as those for the village kids drinking industrially pasteurized milk.)"

Aside from all the studies and theories, aren't there testimonials from raw milk drinkers about health benefits they have received?

Many raw milk drinkers relate personal stories about how their health and that of their families improved after introducing raw milk. At state legislative hearings in Maryland, Vermont, Connecticut, and California, I have heard dozens of people testify about how raw milk improved their health and that of their children. Allergic reactions to pasteurized milk, sometimes diagnosed as lactose intolerance, seemed to clear up with raw milk.

The eagerness of raw milk drinkers to provide testimonials began in late 2006, when a Michigan farmer had his delivery truck raided as he delivered raw milk to members of an Ann Arbor co-op. Some weeks afterwards, when it looked as if the farmer might be charged criminally for violating Michigan's prohibition on sales of raw milk,232 members flooded the local district attorney with testimonials about their positive experiences with the food, as part of their plea with the prosecutor not to file charges against the farmer. One mother, Kristin, wrote: "My son was considered to be lactose intolerant and had numerous ear infections when he drank pasteurized milk. Since he has switched to raw milk, he no longer suffers from ear infections or any other illness. He doesn't seem to get sick like many children his age."

Another mother, Renee, said: "My son is not able to drink pasteurized milk because the enzymes are destroyed in the pasteurization process and his body is not able to metabolize it. We have gone to the emergency room and he has been ill many times because of pasteurized milk. Pasteurized milk causes him to be unable to breathe, and he has had to be put on a nebulizer several times and use an inhaler many times. He also gets eczema from drinking pasteurized milk. Our doctor told us that these things were caused because he was allergic to milk. For years we avoided milk...He can drink raw milk without any of these problems. We have not been to the emergency room once from him drinking raw milk."

The testimonials seemed to have aided the case at hand—the prosecutor eventually decided not to file any charges against the farmer.

Do you know examples of children whose asthma has been helped by raw milk?

Mark McAfee, owner of Organic Pastures Dairy Co., says he frequently hears inspiring stories from parents of asthmatic children.

He recalled recently on my blog meeting at a 2014 conference on fermentation with the mother of a girl who had a serious asthma problem. She "had been an asthma sufferer with frequent ER visits, associated lung infections, ear infections and horrible allergies. After drinking OPDC raw milk...her asthma had been reduced to light occasional allergy, no more medications, no more ear infections, no more antibiotics, no more ER visits!"

This mother was just one of several who told him about their children's positive health experiences. "One after another each of these mothers thanked me for literally saving their kids' lives."

Much of the discussion about health benefits has focused on asthma and allergies. Is there anything to stories I've heard that raw milk can help reduce the symptoms of autism?

A small study out of Saudi Arabia [18], published in early 2014, offers some encouragement on the autism front. Scientists studied the potential benefits of camel milk, which has long been consumed in the Middle East for its perceived health benefits.

In the Saudi study, 45 children with autism were divided into three groups of 15; one was given raw camel milk, one was given boiled camel milk, and a third was given a placebo, for a total of two weeks. The results? "Camel milk administered for two weeks significantly improved clinical measurements of autism severity," the authors concluded. Those that consumed raw camel milk did better on one test measurement. "Subsequent studies are recommended."

Are there any testimonials you are aware of for camel milk and autism?

In late 2013, the scholarly journal, *Global Advances in Health and Medicine*, published an article [19] by the mother of a boy with autism, about his remarkable progress after he started on camel milk. The mother, Christina F. Adams, recounted how she consulted with her physician so he could write what amounted to a prescription to order the camel milk from a supplier she had found in Israel:

"On October 10, 2007, 2 weeks before my son's tenth birthday, he drank his first half cup (4 oz) of thawed raw unheated camel milk....On the morning after my son ingested camel milk, he demonstrated astonishing improvements in behavior including eye contact, communication, emotional expression ('I really love you; you're awesome; you do so much for me'), and self-organization. He ate breakfast more neatly, noted his schedule, put on his shoes, and got his backpack for school while conversing at the same time.

"He continued consuming 4 oz of camel milk daily with rapid continued improvement in behavior and motor planning. For example, he started looking both ways when crossing streets and parking lots. His erratic behavior stopped, and my frequent offerings of extra protein, which had only somewhat mitigated the problem, were no longer needed. Within 3 weeks, there was also a marked improvement and smoothing of his skin condition. Increasing the daily amount of camel milk to 8 oz seemed to cause new facial grimaces and jerking in one arm, which disappeared when his intake returned to 4 oz. His pragmatic language and vocabulary skills were improved, and other academic skills tested above average and exceptional in some areas.

"Interruption of camel milk consumption on several occasions resulted in behavioral and physiological lapses. Just before he turned 12, while I was away from home for two and a half weeks, he did not take camel milk. His school behavior deteriorated to the point that he was in danger of being moved to a special education classroom. Within 24 hours of resuming the camel milk intake, he returned to prior functioning levels."

Is it not possible to get favorable results treating autism with cow milk?

I have heard stories from moms who say raw milk helped their autistic children. But nothing as definitive and dramatic as what Christina Adams reported.

Is there a way to more easily access camel milk than ordering it from Israel?

Yes, a number of American farmers, mostly Amish, have begun raising camels and supplying camel milk. But camels are more difficult to domesticate than cows, and don't give as much milk. As a result, the milk they yield is in high demand, and very expensive, as much as $100 a gallon or more.

Before having an anxiety attack about the potential cost, remember that Adams was giving her son only four ounces a day, not the many glasses that children can consume of cow milk. In fact, her son reacted negatively to a doubling of his camel milk dosage. (For more information on buying raw milk of all kinds, see Chapter 9.)

What are some other medical conditions that raw milk may help?

In my experience, people are drawn to raw milk when they or their children have a health problem of one sort or another that conventional medicines seem unable to help. One notable example is when very young children experience the terrible discomfort of eczema (itching from patches of red and dried skin).

Kristin Canty recounts in the documentary she produced, "Farmageddon", that, as a baby, one of her children had a terrible case of eczema. None of the medications prescribed by doctors worked, and she was at her wit's end. Finally, she heard about possible benefits from raw milk, and her child found relief.

Hilary Boynton, co-author of *The Heal Your Gut Cookbook*, recalls in the book a similar nightmare with an infant son who had serious eczema for the first three years of his life. She tried all kinds of medications, "But still, my son's eczema flared."

A friend suggested raw milk.

"Huh? What was raw milk? Did she mean . . . unpasteurized? Certainly that could not be good for us. But I was at my wit's end, so I went for it. And guess what? It worked! The eczema was subdued, with real food alone!"

What about raw milk for Crohn's disease (a chronic inflammation of the intestines or esophagus)?

I have seen some inspiring online testimonials from young people who say raw milk "cured" them of Crohn's, which can be a debilitating chronic inflammation of the intestines or esophagus. Max Kane, a Wiscsonsin technology entrepreneur (founder of the service, FarmMatch) and also a food rights activist, recounts in talks and speeches how he used raw milk to transform himself from a skinny 18-year-old with Crohn's into the healthy strapping 30-something adult he is today.

Have the various studies and testimonials caused those in the medical or public health communities to change their views of raw milk?

As I indicated earlier in this chapter, there have been some tentative acknowledgments of some of the studies. At the same time, there has been controversy within the medical and research communities about some of the claims made on behalf of raw milk.

One notable example has been about the frequent claim made by raw milk drinkers that it relieved their lactose intolerance, which is a difficulty with digesting lactose, a key component of milk. It comes out as a digestive problem with bloating, nausea, gas.

The idea that raw milk might relieve lactose intolerance has huge implications, since the FDA has estimated that between 30 million and 50 million Americans are sufferers. The possibility gained traction in 2008 when two Michigan raw milk supporters—retired pathologist Ted Beals and Michigan lawyer Steve Bemis—conducted a survey of raw milk drinkers to find individuals who had been advised by physicians that they were lactose intolerant.

They found 155 such individuals, of whom 127, or 82%, said they had no symptoms of lactose intolerance when they drank raw milk. That study, which was unpublished, encouraged raw milk supporters to fund a study at Stanford, to seek more "official" confirmation of the findings.

In 2014, a medical researcher at Stanford published the results of a "pilot study" [20] of 16 individuals with confirmed lactose intolerance who were fed raw milk and pasteurized milk over eight-day segments.

It was thumbs down on the possibility that raw milk relieved lactose intolerance, concluding: "Raw milk failed to reduce lactose malabsorption or lactose intolerance symptoms compared with pasteurized milk among adults positive for lactose malabsorption. These results do not support widespread anecdotal claims that raw milk reduces the symptoms of lactose intolerance."

How could there be such a disconnect between the Michigan research results and the Stanford study?

The only thing I could figure out was that many people who have difficulty digesting ordinary pasteurized milk likely have some other problem besides lactose intolerance--possibly an allergic reaction of some kind. If you look at the Stanford study in some detail, you learn that 440 people responded to Stanford's call for volunteers suffering from symptoms of lactose intolerance. But when all was said and done, and people were eliminated for various reasons—primarily failing the hydrogen test (to clinically determine lactose intolerance), 95% of the volunteers were disqualified.

It might be said that the Stanford study was flawed, since it was designed to make it very difficult for many potential participants to be accepted.

If you are correct, doesn't the small number of study participants who qualified as lactose intolerant call into question the FDA's estimate that 30 million to 50 million people suffer from lactose intolerance?

Most definitely. My feeling is that many of the people who have problems digesting pasteurized dairy products don't suffer from lactose intolerance in a clinical sense, and would not have qualified for the Stanford study.

The Michigan study suggests that many of these people can somehow handle raw milk easier than pasteurized milk.

Is there any scientific evidence to suggest that pasteurized milk might itself cause allergic reactions that could be mistaken for lactose intolerance?

There have been two small studies I am aware of:

-A 1988 double blind study of five children with allergic reactions to cow milk had them tested with raw milk, pasteurized milk, and pasteurized and homogenized milk, and noted in the journal *Allergy* [21] "an increased ability of pasteurized and homogenized/pasteurized milk to evoke allergic reactions in patients allergic to milk."

-A 2008 study of mice on allergic reactions, published in the journal *Allergy* [22], was entitled, "Pasteurization of milk proteins promotes allergic sensitizations..."

Just as no follow-up has occurred in the U.S. on the European raw milk studies on asthma and allergies, there has been no follow-up on these two studies indicating that pasteurized milk could be promoting allergic reactions.

What other controversies are there about health claims for raw milk?

There are medical people who say Crohn's disease may be caused by a bacteria that comes from both pasteurized and raw milk. This view gained currency from a doctor who wrote in *Psychology Today* [23] that she seems to be "one of the few people in the world who can claim to be 'cured' of Crohn's disease." Her cure? Long term treatment with antibiotics.

Since the bacteria that causes Crohn's originates in milk, under her theory, she urged readers to "remember that... when you go to the grocery store and consider buying raw milk products."

Similarly, when Christina Adams came out with the favorable results her autistic son achieved with camel milk, a clinical psychologist, Travis Thompson, took issue in a Facebook post [24]: "Parents, please, please do not take any of Ms. Adams' report as evidence camel's milk has any benefit in autism whatsoever. The complex hodgepodge of interventions the child was given, the child's previous substantial benefit from ABA therapy, and complete lack of any objective assessment of the child's behavior before and after drinking camel's milk makes any claim of benefit... meaningless."

Why is the evidence on raw milk and health benefits so complicated and contradictory?

All I can say is that that seems to be the nature of nearly every aspect of the raw milk debate.

Chapter 6: Reconciling Risks and Benefits

Some years ago, I took a vacation in Costa Rica, and while traveling back roads, I came across a number of corporate banana plantations. On these vast agricultural preserves, most of the banana bunches weighing down the short banana trees were covered with blue plastic bags.

When I inquired with an individual fruit seller I happened to meet, he explained that the bags were meant to douse the bananas with fungicides to prevent diseases. They not only coat the bananas, but sicken the plantation workers he said. This fruit seller was peddling organic bananas, which he said didn't grow with the blue plastic bags and fungicide.

That banana experience made such a deep impression on me that I resolved never again to buy anything but organic bananas, and I never have. Indeed, it made me more committed than ever to feeding myself and my family organic fruits and veggies whenever possible. To me, the prospect of ingesting or feeding to my family foods tinged with fungicides and pesticides, even in very small quantities via residues, is something I consider too risky to tolerate. My instincts tell me those tiny bits of residue, day after day, week after week, accumulate over the months and years and cause cancer and other serious health conditions.

That's me and how I respond to perceived risk.

I know other smart discriminating people who pooh-pooh my concerns about conventionally-raised fruits and vegetables. They regularly shop at the mass-market grocery stores and buy the bananas I avoid, without a second thought, because they are cheaper than the organic variety. These individuals assume that America's regulatory authorities would not allow their sale if these foods were seriously risky.

However, some of these same people will read a newspaper account of children becoming terribly sick from pathogens picked up at a petting zoo [1] with cows and goats, and resolve never to take their children or grandchildren to a petting zoo. To them, it's preferable to deny their children the pleasures of a petting zoo than risk even the slightest chance they will become sick with a pathogen.

I will read the same newspaper account, and, while I'll feel terribly for the victims, decide that such occurrences are so exceedingly rare that I'm not going to deny my grandchildren the pleasure of going to the petting area of a zoo. Rather, I'll try to reduce the odds even further—in this kind of situation by insisting the children carefully wash their hands with soap and water immediately upon leaving the petting area.

Notice I haven't said anything about raw milk. I recount these situations to illustrate how differently people assess risk.

So how does such risk assessment apply to raw milk?

Some people read about children becoming seriously ill from raw milk, and conclude that if even a single child gets very sick from raw milk, that's enough to veto the food forever from their homes. In their view, the likely health benefits just aren't great enough to justify taking the risk of serious illness. There are so many risks out there, in this view, that it isn't necessary to add another.

Other people read the same information and conclude

that the occurrences are so exceedingly rare they shouldn't force such a radical decision as banning an important food from their lives. These parents decide that the chances of their children experiencing positive health benefits from raw milk are much greater than the chances of them getting seriously ill.

What is your view?

I should say that I respect both these views.

Personally, I have decided that raw milk is highly nutritious, and likely helps strengthen my immune system enough that I reduce the odds of getting other diseases. (Mind you, I haven't said I can't get these diseases, just that I believe I lower the risk.) I have also concluded that the very occasional examples of serious illness from raw milk played up by the news media are so unusual that the risk of illness is worth taking for me personally as well as for my family.

As for serving raw milk to children, I personally would do that if my children were young enough. (I didn't know about raw milk when they were growing up.) Others of my family members don't agree with me on this, and as I said, I respect their decisions as parents to not serve their children raw milk. (More on this issue of divisions within families in Chapter 10.)

As upsetting as the stories I see in the news media are about people sickened by raw milk pathogens, I'd rather make my decisions based on the data and not on the basis of a very few scary stories about one particular food.

What does the data tell you?

I think I intuitively feel the repeated exposure to small amounts of poison (such as pesticide residues in fruits and vegetables) is much riskier over a long period of time than the chances of encountering especially dangerous pathogens in a particular food. Just looking at the odds--the chances of getting cancer are far from remote, less than one in ten for breast cancer (for women) and prostate cancer (for men). The chances of getting sick from raw milk are quite remote—at most one in 100,000 and, more likely, one in a million or more. (It's difficult to be precise because data on raw milk consumption in the U.S. is incomplete.)

Is one in 100,000 really so remote?

I know that even if I get sick from raw milk, the impact of the illness will very likely be much lower than if I am diagnosed with cancer, since the odds are overwhelming that the raw milk illness will be mild; my chances of becoming so sick from raw milk that I, or a family member, needs to be hospitalized are one in some millions.

How did you come up with that range of odds?

Nutritionist Chris Kressler did an intriguing analysis in 2012 [2]. He made the point that most illnesses from tainted food, including raw milk, are mild, with a few days of upset stomach. Then he added:

"The statistic we should be more concerned with is hospitalizations for serious illnesses such as kidney failure and hemolytic uremic syndrome (HUS) caused by unpasteurized milk. This does happen, and children and the elderly are particularly vulnerable and more likely to experience a serious illness. That said, hospitalizations from raw milk are extremely rare. During the 2000 – 2007 period, there were 12 hospitalizations for illnesses associated with raw fluid milk. That's an average of 1.5 per year. With approximately 9.4 million people drinking raw milk, that means you have about a 1 in 6 million chance of being hospitalized from drinking raw milk.

"To put this in perspective, according to the U.S. Department of Transportation [3], you have a roughly 1 in 8,000 chance of dying in a motor vehicle accident if you live in the U.S. Therefore, you have a 750 times greater chance of dying in a car crash than becoming hospitalized from drinking raw milk."

Or, as I noted, men have a one in six chance of being diagnosed with prostate cancer, and women a one in eight chance of being diagnosed with breast cancer.

Are you suggesting that raw milk isn't any riskier than pasteurized milk?

No, I personally think raw milk poses a greater risk of illness than pasteurized milk. But I say that, convinced that neither food is especially risky. The nonprofit Center for Science and the Public Interest (CSPI) ranks the dairy category, which includes both pasteurized and unpasteurized milk, as the least risky of eight food categories [4], based on illnesses monitored from 2002-2011. In this analysis, vegetables are 4.3 times more risky than dairy, chicken and other poultry 7.4 times more risky, and seafood 19.7 times more dangerous.

The Center for Science and the Public Interest notes

that while dairy is among the least risky of food categories, dairy did trend upwards [5] in 2010, likely based on "the increased availability of raw, unpasteurized milk and cheese…"

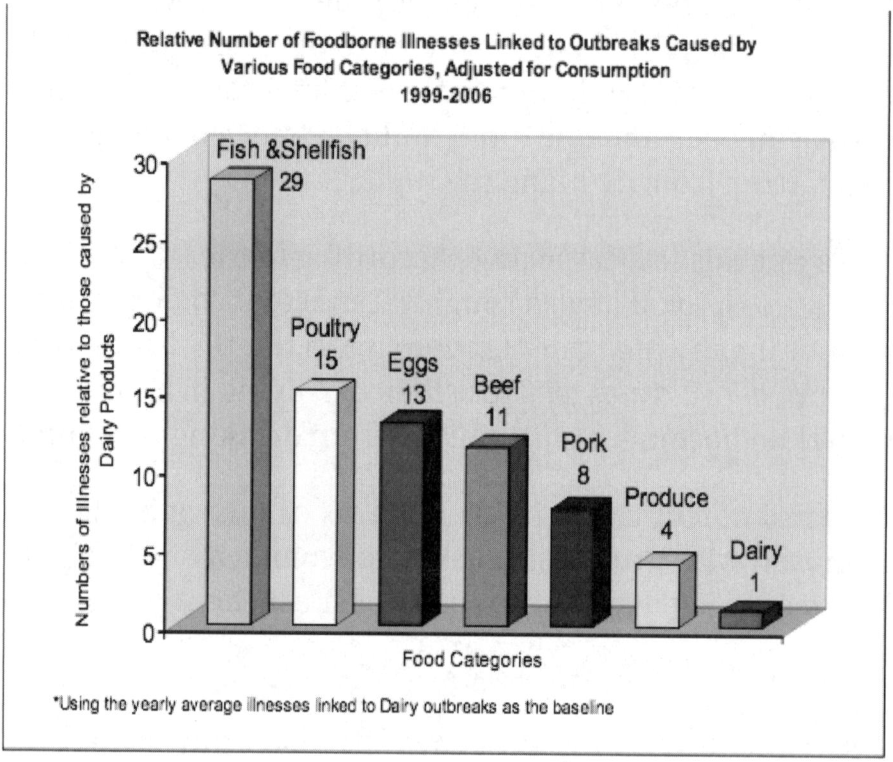

If raw milk is riskier than pasteurized milk, aren't children more in danger, since they disproportionately consume so much milk?

Yes, children are more susceptible. And, indeed, the CDC says [6] that "a substantial proportion of the raw milk-associated disease burden falls on children; among the 104 outbreaks from 1998-2011 with information on the patients' ages available, 82% involved at least one person younger than 20 years old."

It sounds from the CDC information that the risk for children from raw milk may be greater than you originally suggested. Is that correct?

Not necessarily. Unfortunately, the CDC presents its data about children being especially at risk from raw milk in isolation. So we don't know the actual percentage of individuals under age 20 sickened out of total food-borne illnesses, or the trends year to year or state to state. We don't know how the data on children getting sick from raw milk compares to data from pasteurized milk. I would presume children are just as susceptible when there are illnesses from pasteurized milk, since children are the main consumers of pasteurized milk as well. How do other foods stack up in terms of their risk to children? When there are illnesses from bologna and salami, for example, what percentage of the victims are children? (I raise the example of deli meats because they tend to be highly risky for illness compared to other foods.)

Aren't you just looking for ways to avoid coming down on raw milk?

No, I'm mainly frustrated by the incomplete nature of the CDC data. As just one example, I have reviewed data on serious illnesses from raw milk (involving E.coli 0157:H7), and discovered that the area where I live, the Northeast, has had one outbreak of serious illness since 2000. It affected 14 people (three of them children), in 2008 in Connecticut. Three children seriously sickened over 15 years isn't a terribly serious risk, statistically speaking.

It's possible that other areas of the country have a more pressing problem—there have been serious illnesses associated with raw milk since 2005 scattered around the country, in Tennessee, Kentucky, Washington, Oregon, and California.

Still and all, I can't say for certain what this observation says compared to serious illnesses from other foods, because such data isn't readily available.

Why do geographical trends matter?

If you live in a state like Massachusetts or New Hampshire or Vermont or Maine, where raw milk is legal and regulated, and which hasn't had a serious illness from raw milk in at least 15 years (and probably longer), then you can reasonably conclude, as a parent, that the risk of serving raw milk to your children is quite low.

Didn't the CDC conclude that raw milk is 150 times riskier than pasteurized milk?

Yes, that is how most of the media interpreted the results of research the agency put out in 2012 [7]. But once again, it wasn't so straightforward. The CDC's calculation was based on the number of outbreaks, not the number of illnesses. An outbreak can be as few as two illnesses, on up to thousands. Because pasteurized milk is distributed so widely, outbreaks have involved thousands of illnesses. But pasteurized milk causes relatively few outbreaks. It's the opposite with raw milk—more outbreaks, but with usually just a handful of people affected.

Well, on the other extreme, I have heard claims that raw milk is actually safer than pasteurized milk, because the milk from cows fed only grass actually kills off pathogens. What does the data say about that claim?

You may have heard the old saying, "Lies, damned lies, and statistics." In other words, statistics can be manipulated in all kinds of ways. Nowhere are they manipulated more than in the world of raw milk. The manipulation is reflective of just how emotionally charged the subject of raw milk has become.

A big proponent of the claim that raw milk is safer than pasteurized milk has come from Ted Beals, a retired pathologist who taught at the University of Michigan and has spent years studying and analyzing data on foodborne illness, with a special focus on raw milk. In an analysis he presented to a conference of the Weston A. Price Foundation, which encourages consumption of raw milk, he came to this stark conclusion [8] about the risk of raw milk versus the risk of driving to the farm:

"I have performed the calculations based on national highway safety data and the data on foodborne illness attributed to drinking raw milk. It can be shown that I have a greater risk of being injured in the car driving to the farm to obtain milk for myself and my wife, than becoming ill from the fresh unprocessed whole milk. And we drink a lot of that delicious and healthy milk every day."

So how did Beals come up with his calculation that raw milk is safer than pasteurized milk?

He claimed raw milk is one of the safest foods around, based on data he says show there have been an average of

42 illnesses each year from raw milk between 1999 and 2011. "Using this average of 42 illnesses per year, we can show, using government figures, that you are about 35,000 times more likely to become ill from other foods than you are from raw milk."

What was the problem with his assessment?

It comes in his statement, "we can show, using government figures" that we are 35,000 times more likely to become ill from other foods than raw milk. Those "government figures" included estimates of total food-borne illness, showing 48 million estimated illnesses each year. Those estimates are based on the assumption that reported illnesses understate the actual total of illnesses, since many are unreported. Thus, Beals was comparing 42 average reported illnesses for raw milk against millions of estimated illnesses—a potentially misleading comparison. (His calculation of 42 average annual reported illnesses from raw milk is based on his own data assessment, in which he excluded a number of reported illnesses where he decided the cause of illness may not have come from raw milk, but possibly from other sources, like pre-pasteurized milk intended for commercial processing).

So what is the risk of illness from raw milk versus pasteurized milk?

The distinction between outbreaks versus illnesses in the CDC analysis estimating raw milk to be 150 times more dangerous than pasteurized milk prompted Chris Kresser, the nutritionist, to do his own calculations [9] about the CDC's assessment: "It's true that you have a higher chance of getting sick from drinking raw milk than pasteurized milk. But the risk is **9.4 times higher, not 150 times higher as the CDC claimed.**"

Well, isn't a risk of more than nine times from raw milk pretty serious?

Kresser anticipated the obvious concern, and explained that it all comes down to the specifics of the risk: "When you hear that you have a roughly 9 times greater (relative) risk of getting sick from drinking raw milk than pasteurized milk, that might sound scary. And indeed it would be, if we were talking about the absolute risk moving from 5% to 45%.

"But when the absolute risk is extremely small, as it is here, a relative nine-fold increase is rather insignificant. If you have a 0.00011 percent chance of getting sick from drinking pasteurized milk, and a 9.4 times greater risk of getting sick from drinking unpasteurized milk, we're still talking about **a miniscule risk of 0.00106% (one one-thousandth of a percent).**" (emphasis by the author)

What about other aspects of risk assessment. Should people be concerned about trying to strengthen their children's immune systems, to protect against asthma and allergies?

This is a big part of my concern. Immune system disorders like asthma and allergies are much more prevalent than they were years ago. Today, nearly one in ten children has asthma.

The question assumed greater urgency in late 2014, as hundreds of children were infected by something known as the Enterovirus D68. It is the same type of virus as the one that caused widespread polio outbreaks during the first half of last century. This latest version was apparently most threatening to children, with severe respiratory complications striking children with compromised immune systems and asthma. Given that raw milk has been shown to help counter asthma, it would seem to make sense as a potential antidote for Enterovirus D68.

What does the explosion of immune-system conditions have to do with raw milk?

There is growing concern in the science and medical communities that the rise in immune-system disorders may be the result of an overly sterile environment, which reduces children's exposure to infections as well as "good bacteria," often present in natural foods and even "dirt"—something that has come to be known as "the hygiene hypothesis."

According to the Mayo Clinic [10]: "The hygiene hypothesis proposes that childhood exposure to germs and certain infections helps the immune system develop. This teaches the body to differentiate harmless substances from the harmful substances that trigger asthma. In theory, exposure to certain germs teaches the immune system not to overreact."

So let's get to the real question that concerns those of us who are parents: Should I feed my children raw milk?

This is perhaps the ultimate question for a natural food newbie. In my view, the decision is ultimately a personal one. Parents who decide in favor of feeding their children raw milk usually decide that the potential health benefits of raw milk, such as protection against asthma, outweigh the possible risks. Those who decide against raw milk conclude the opposite—that the risks of illness from pathogens outweigh any possible health benefits.

How sick can people get from raw milk?

Generally speaking, raw milk won't make adults all that sick. I know of only two cases over the last ten years in which adults have become seriously ill—both because of complications from *Campylobacter*.

But raw milk can, and has, made a handful of young children very ill since 2006. All the children experienced complications from E.coli O157:H7—a condition known as hemolytic uremic syndrome (HUS).

Without getting into all the technical terminology of what goes on in the body, HUS can seriously weaken the kidneys, so that a number of the sick children have wound up on dialysis for several days, up to a few weeks, until their kidneys recovered.

That being said, nearly all of those cases appear to have resulted from dairies that had some kind of sanitation/ safety issue.

Can you provide an example of children becoming sick?

Raw milk opponents have worked to publicize the cases of illness, to the extent that the CDC created a web site [11] featuring interviews with individuals made sick, including parents of two sickened children.

The worst outbreak of the last decade occurred at Foundation Farm in Washington State, where 19 people were sickened, of whom 15 were youths; four wound up with kidney failure. One of the children, two-year-old Kylee Young, became so sick she had a stroke and had to have part of her colon removed. She would eventually receive a successful kidney transplant from her mother. But Kylee will likely have developmental and health problems for many years.

Foundation Farm's owners were inexperienced, having only been at it a few years. They were milking their cows without running water. Added to that, they were milking their cows in and around the mud of spring season, which happens to be the time of year when cows are likeliest to shed E.coli 0157:H7.

The images I've seen on the Internet of those little children who got terribly sick from raw milk—all hooked up to tubes on dialysis-- are very disturbing. Shouldn't we be concerned if even a single child becomes terribly ill?

We definitely should be concerned. And some people in the raw milk business became concerned enough they formed an organization in 2011 known as The Raw Milk Institute (RAWMI) [12] to set strict safety standards for raw dairies, and only certify those dairies that have passed a tough inspection that shows them to be complying with the standards.

It is an unfortunate fact of life that, even with the strictest safety standards, people will continue to get sick from raw milk, as they will from pasteurized milk and all other foods as well. The goal of all raw milk producers, and all food producers, must be to do everything they can to reduce the number of illnesses as much as possible. In my experience, producers of raw dairy feel that way—after all, there is no worse way to hurt your business than for people to become seriously ill.

In the end, you as a consumer, and possibly as a parent as well, must make the decision about whether you can tolerate the risk associated with raw milk.

If raw milk is riskier than pasteurized milk, even by a small amount, isn't it an open-and-shut case--shouldn't I just choose the pasteurized milk?

It may be, once again, depending on your views of risk and health. If the possibility of pathogens in your food creates undue anxiety, then pasteurized milk may well be your best choice.

In my view, risks from food safety are about more than the possibility of pathogens being present. While pathogens pose risk in all foods, so does processing and the inclusion of sugar and artificial colorings and other ingredients. There are even medical experts now saying that sugar is like a poison.

Moreover, for meat, eggs, and dairy, I worry about pesticides, additives, antibiotic residues and GMO ingredients being present in the animal feed. When I buy raw milk from a farmer whom I know doesn't use antibiotics, and who raises his or her cows entirely on grass that hasn't been treated with pesticides, I feel as if I am getting a safer food than is available via factory farm producers.

What is it that convinces you to recommend raw milk despite these tragedies?

Remember, I am not trying to be an advocate for raw milk. I am an advocate for people being able to make their own informed risk assessments, and choices based on those assessments. If they conclude that raw milk is just so risky that it makes them uncomfortable, then they shouldn't consume raw milk or serve it to their families, in my view.

My own comfort level with raw milk stems from my conviction that raw milk can be produced safely, that it isn't inherently unsafe. From my experience, the tragedies that have occurred have resulted from farms using unsafe practices. The farms with the worst experiences, like Foundation Farm in Washington, were forced by the tragedies to shut down. You can be sure that other raw dairy producers took note, and resolved to learn. Indeed, Charlotte Smith of Champoeg Creamery in Washington says she keeps a photo of Kylee Young, the girl so seriously sickened at Foundation Farm, in her milk room, as a reminder of the importance of producing the safest possible raw milk.

How did these tragedies not show raw milk to be inherently unsafe?

This is a question I would answer with a couple of other

questions: If raw milk is inherently unsafe, how is it that hundreds of thousands of people are consuming it every day without getting sick? How is it that many thousands of people have been drinking it in any number of states without so much as a single illness over a decade or more?

What else convinced you that raw milk isn't inherently unsafe?

The pathogens of today aren't nearly as lethal as those of the nineteenth century—things like typhus, brucellosis, tuberculosis. Those pathogens created widespread serious illness, involving hundreds and even thousands of people, and often killed their victims. There were no antibiotics to treat victims. There were no vaccines to provide protection.

Today's pathogens are nothing to be sneezed at, but they aren't anything approaching the same category as those of the 1800s. Today's pathogens that can infect raw milk are the same as those that taint other foods, which mostly create an unpleasant stomach upset, but generally don't kill. The four main ones are *Campylobacter*, *Salmonella*, *Listeria*, and *E. coli* 0157:H7 (which is the most dangerous).

The most common pathogen to infect people from raw milk is *Campylobacter*, which mostly causes stomach upset, and almost never kills. Probably the largest outbreak of illness from raw milk over the last decade was in 2012 from *Campylobacter*, and involved a Pennsylvania raw dairy; it sickened 80 people, all of whom recovered completely, and when the dairy re-opened after the illnesses, business was better than ever as most customers were quite willing to trust the dairy's commitment to improving its safety precautions.

The CDC reported in a late-2014 study [13] of illnesses from raw milk that more than 80% of the illnesses in the six years between 2007 and 2012 were from *Campylobacter*.

Another common pathogen is *Listeria monocytogenes*, which can kill, and cause miscarriages in pregnant women, but hasn't been known to cause a single illness in fluid raw milk in more than a decade, and only rarely shows up in raw milk cheese. Indeed, it is more common in pasteurized milk and pasteurized milk cheese; in 2007, *Listeria* in pasteurized milk from a small Massachusetts dairy killed three adults; in 2013, there were two serious outbreaks from *Listeria monocytogenes*—one from a Delaware producer and the other from a Wisconsin producer—in pasteurized milk cheese that hospitalized 12 and killed two. Among those hospitalized were three newborn babies.

There is also *Salmonella*, which rarely infects raw milk. That leaves *E. coli* O157:H7, which doesn't occur often in raw milk, but when it does can be very serious. Only discovered by scientists in 1982, it is a scourge of our factory farming system, and has shown up not only in raw milk, but ground beef, raw spinach, and a variety of other foods.

The actual illness from *E. coli* O157:H7 isn't much different from *Campylobacter*—what makes it different are the potential complications of a small percentage of children (less than 10%) developing hemolytic uremic syndrome (HUS) [14]. According to the same CDC study I referred to earlier in this answer about *Campylobacter*, *E. coli* O157:H7 was a distant second in raw milk illnesses, accounting for about 17%.

Chapter 7: How Do I Go About Buying Raw Milk?

The title of this chapter is one you would not find about any other food. Raw milk is, after all, the only food that is so heavily regulated it isn't easily available in many places.

Indeed, its availability varies widely from state to state, and even within certain states. That is partly a function of regulation. It is also a function of the uneven location of dairies producing raw milk.

This chapter's title also suggests a related question: How do I go about locating safe raw milk? Defining availability and safety are more complicated than one would think, and so they get separate chapters.

How do I even go about finding raw milk? It's not carried in any of the supermarkets I use.

Raw milk is regulated at the state level, except for a federal law that prohibits the shipment and sale across state borders. So each state has its own regulations--in effect, we have 50 different sets of regulations.

That sounds confusing—are the rules pretty similar, with just minor variations?

No, the rules differ widely. So the practical effect is a lot of confusion, and widely varying availability of raw milk. For example, raw milk is allowed for sale in retail stores in Connecticut, as well as off the farm. It isn't allowed for sale at all in its neighbor to the north, Rhode Island. And Rhode Island's neighbor to the north, Massachusetts, allows something in between-- limited sale of raw milk, directly from dairy farms that have a permit.

Even within a state, there can be variations. For example, while California allows retail sales of raw milk, two of the state's counties prohibit any such sales.

About half of Massachusetts' towns have ordinances that prohibit raw milk, so farms in those towns can't sell raw milk via the state permit program unless they get their towns to change the local law. A few have done so after heavy local lobbying; in 2010, Framingham, MA, residents convinced the town's health board to approve raw milk sales, which allowed a local farm to offer it for sale. The same thing happened in the town of Groton, MA, in 2014.

You mentioned Rhode Island as an example of a state that doesn't allow sales of raw milk. Are there others?

Some 15 states explicitly prohibit raw milk sales. In addition to Rhode Island, those states include New Jersey, North Carolina, Delaware, Maryland, Nevada, Iowa, Louisiana, West Virginia, Hawaii, Montana, Kentucky, Alabama, Indiana, and Virginia.

How do people in those states obtain raw milk?

Usually in one of two ways:

1. People in "dry" states that are easily accessible to states that allow raw milk simply travel to a neighboring state for their milk. Thus, people in New Jersey and Maryland, which prohibit raw milk sales, often travel to Pennsylvania, where raw milk is widely available. One large raw dairy in Pennsylvania actually has "drop sites" around

Pennsylvania, including a few right on the New Jersey border.

2. At least four of the 15 states that prohibit public raw milk sales—Virginia, Kentucky, Indiana, and Alabama--have tacitly allow it via private sharing arrangements known as "herd shares" or "cow shares," whereby individuals buy a share of a farmer's herd and then pay a regular "boarding" fee that allows them a gallon or two of milk each week. And at least four other states--Wyoming, Michigan, Ohio, and Colorado—actually have formal policies or legislation allowing herd share or cow share arrangements.

Why would states that essentially ban the sale of raw milk suddenly allow its distribution via a private arrangement?

A few of these states have come around to the view, pushed by advocates of raw milk, that people have a right to enter into private contracts with farmers to buy food, since contracts are a fundamental means of transacting business for all manner of goods and services in the U.S. What these people have argued is that private contractual sales of raw milk are outside the public sphere represented by supermarkets, convenience stores, and other retail outlets. Thus, raw milk obtained privately is limited to those who seriously want it and are willing to enter into private agreements to obtain it.

A few states have been forced to accept private arrangements. For example, Ohio, which for many years prohibited raw milk sales, only relented after a state judge in 2006 ruled in favor of a dairy farmer who contested the state's crackdown on her herd share. The judge ruled the state's objections to herd shares were vague and inconsistent; when the state didn't appeal the judge's ruling, the herd shares became legal, and are now widely available throughout Ohio.

In Michigan, another state that long prohibited raw milk sales, the state's attorney general in 2007 decided to allow herd shares after a public outcry that resulted when state agriculture regulators confiscated $8,000 of unpasteurized milk from a farmer on his way to make a delivery to shareholders.

Of course, some states persist in preventing raw milk distribution in any form. Notable among these is Maryland, where, a few years back, the state's supreme court ruled herd share and cow share arrangements illegal under state law. And despite extensive and high-publicity organizing by raw milk advocates, and a sympathetic view by many legislators, the Maryland legislature in 2014 yet again refused to consider legislation that would allow herd shares.

Wouldn't it be economically beneficial for individual states to allow raw milk sales?

Yes, it is excellent business, for both dairy owners and local consumers. When people buy raw milk locally, the money doesn't go to some distant corporate monopoly, but rather stays in the community. The local dairy gets all the revenue, and uses it to buy supplies and new equipment, and hire workers. Moreover, when people buy milk from a local farmer, they invariably buy other food, like eggs, butter, meat, and veggies. So instead of a $10 or $20 purchase every week for milk, you are often talking about a $100 or $150 purchase every week. Multiply that by 52 weeks a year, and you can see why the big dairy producers and retail grocery chains don't like the idea of more people getting too familiar with buying raw milk directly from farmers.

Sally Fallon, the head of the Weston A. Price Foundation and owner of a dairy farm in Maryland, has done some calculations that her home state loses likely $90 million in farm food sales to neighboring Pennsylvania because of Maryland's prohibition of raw milk sales. When you add the related economic activity associated with that $90 million circulating through the economy, the total loss to Maryland approaches $250 million annually, she calculates.

In New Jersey, which also prohibits raw milk sales of any kind, the state's dairies could be missing out on potentially $95 million annually just in raw milk sales, according to Joseph Heckman, a professor of soil science at Rutgers University (though he always tells legislators that he is testifying personally, and not as a Rutgers faculty member). As in Maryland, those sales are being lost to neighboring Pennsylvania, Heckman has testified to New Jersey legislators considering the legalization of on-farm sales in the state. (So far, a couple of legislative attempts have stalled.)

How does the federal government feel about these private sales?

There is even more confusion on the federal front. As I said earlier in this chapter, there is a ban on interstate shipment and sale of raw milk. But the FDA has added to the confusion by saying it doesn't consider individuals buying milk in one state and bringing it back to another for their personal use to be violating the federal prohibition.

So individuals who regularly trek from New Jersey and Maryland to Pennsylvania for raw milk don't have to worry about being stopped for violating the law.

But farmers who bring raw milk from one state to another can be considered in violation, even if they are delivering the milk to a member of a food club or a herdshare. The FDA and the U.S. Justice Department in 2012 obtained an injunction against Pennsylvania farmer Daniel Allgyer, who was making deliveries of raw milk to food club members in Maryland, for violating the federal ban. The FDA has even suggested that farmers in states where raw milk is legal and who sell to consumers coming from a state that doesn't allow raw milk could be considered in violation of the interstate ban. The FDA has yet to follow through on that threat.

What are the regulations in my area?

The best way to begin determining what the rules are in your state is to go to www.realmilk.com [1] where you'll find information on each state's regulations.

A U.S. map [2] put together by the Farm-to-Consumer Legal Defense Fund color codes the states according to their regulations.

I live in a state that doesn't allow raw milk sales, but does allow private arrangements, so how do I go about finding a food club or cow share to join so as to obtain raw milk regularly from a particular dairy?

Generally, you have to do some asking around simply to find a cow share or food club. It used to be you could ask for suggestions on various food-related listserves, but users of some of these online services found that government agents were using the services to gather "intelligence" on raw milk, and what the agents considered to be illegal sales. The most notorious case was that involving the Pennsylvania Amish farmer I alluded to earlier in this chapter, Daniel Allgyer, who supplied food clubs in the Washington, D.C. area with raw milk.

In 2009 and 2010, FDA agents from the Baltimore office signed up as members and ordered raw milk from Allgyer. Based on their experiences, the U.S. Justice Department went to federal court in Pennsylvania, and in 2011 obtained a permanent injunction barring Allgyer from selling raw milk across state lines. He decided after that to exit the farming business.

On the other side of the country, agents from the California Department of Food and Agriculture and the Los Angeles County District Attorney infiltrated food clubs in the Los Angeles area. They eventually used information they obtained to organize raids on the Rawesome Food Club in Venice, and a Ventura County farm owned by Sharon Palmer, and charged Palmer and one of her assistants, along with an operator of Rawesome, with a variety of felony charges having to do with selling raw milk without a license.

So how do I find a herd share or food club if everyone is so nervous online?

Kind of the old-fashioned way—you have to ask around with friends you know are interested in buying food locally and direct from farms.

You can also search on the realmilk.com [3] site, or on FarmMatch.com [4] (a site that helps consumers learn about small farms in their areas and what they are selling). Some farms do post information about their herd shares or food clubs on their web sites.

And what kind of process do I have to follow to join a cow share/herd share or a food club?

Technically, a cow share or a herd share involves buying into the herd—you pay an upfront fee, perhaps $50, for a share of a cow, or of the entire herd. You also agree to pay for animal "maintenance." In return, you are rewarded with milk on a regular basis. The maintenance usually translates into a cost per gallon. For example, you may commit to paying $12 a week, which entitles you to a gallon of milk each week.

Some herd shares require a weekly or monthly payment, whether or not you are around to collect your milk, while others allow you to pay only when you actually pick up milk.

Are there any other commitments?

The cow share/herd share documents often contain a clause that absolves the farmer of any financial liability in the event you get sick—kind of like a release from liability at a downhill ski resort. The reality is that these releases aren't usually enforceable, at least for milk. If someone does get sick, courts have generally ruled the release forms aren't enforceable, especially if the victims are children, on the rationale that children can't decide to sign a release form.

What about a food club?

A food club is more straightforward. You generally sign an agreement put together by the farmer providing the food, in which you agree to pay an annual membership fee, usually $25 or $50 a year. The agreement you sign commits you to obeying the club's rules, and sometimes even committing to its philosophy. For example, some food clubs are committed to supplying primarily raw foods, and state that they prohibit not only pasteurized milk, but other foods that might be heated, like processed honey.

Do food clubs have any kind of legal protection, like herd shares?

Food clubs are another way of distributing food privately. But they don't necessarily have the same legal protection of herd shares, since the contractual connection isn't as tight.

However, when state regulators in Minnesota and Wisconsin challenged farmers selling raw milk via food clubs in 2010, 2011, and 2012, the clubs gained legal backing. In both those states, regulators argued that the food clubs amounted to retail sellers, and thus required food retailing licenses. Since both states prohibited retail sale of raw milk, the demand that the farmers obtain such a license amounted to an effort to put them out of business.

When the farmers refused to obtain licenses, and continued selling to their club members, the states filed criminal misdemeanor charges against the farmers. In jury trials in 2012 and 2013, both farmers—Alvin Schlangen of Minnesota and Vernon Hershberger of Wisconsin—were acquitted of the licensing charges, and they continue to sell raw milk.

Isn't there an easier way of obtaining raw milk—delivery to my door, for example, like the old-fashioned milk man?

If you live in a state like Vermont, home delivery of raw milk is allowed. But Vermont is one of the few states that specifically allow it.

In some states that require purchases be made directly from farms, customers have banded together to organize car pools or even delivery services to obtain their milk more conveniently. Some of these services are in somewhat of a gray area, legally speaking.

It does sound cumbersome to have to go to a farm store, or to meet a farmer at a drop site, to obtain your food. But in reality, when people buy raw milk from a farmer, they often buy other food like eggs, meat, cheese, and vegetables. So going to a drop site or a farm store once a week or every two weeks isn't necessarily all that different from taking a weekly trip to the supermarket.

But I'll still have to go to the supermarket to obtain certain items like cleaning materials or nuts and fruits. Aren't I really committing to a major shift in my food life by seeking out raw milk?

Yes, you are committing to an important shift in how you obtain food. You are committing to supporting local farming. You will usually meet up with other people who care as much about their food as you do. And you will be spending more time planning what food to buy and actually obtaining your food—hopefully time you decide is well spent based on sourcing food that is likelier fresher, safer, and more nutritious than what you were obtaining at the supermarket.

But if I live in a state where raw milk can be sold at retail, don't I just need to go to a local grocery store to find it?

Not exactly. In California and Connecticut, where raw milk can be sold at retail, you will mostly find it at health food stores rather than regular grocery stores. In New Hampshire, it is available at several food co-ops that sell food at retail. It's also possible in the states that sell at retail to buy raw milk at farmers markets.

One major retailer, Whole Foods, that used to carry raw milk (in states that allowed its sale) discontinued carrying it in any of its stores in 2008, after several Connecticut children became ill from raw milk.

It's also possible in those retail states to buy it directly from farms that have permits to sell at retail.

It sounds complicated. How do I locate a farm I would like?

It is complicated in many places. For example, California has only two dairies licensed to sell raw milk at retail. While they have good retail distribution, the milk is not necessarily going to be for everyone's taste. As a result, California also has an estimated 500 or more very small farms that have no licenses, but sell their milk privately, via herd share or cow share arrangements.

Pennsylvania has a permit system whereby dairies can sell raw milk directly to consumers who come to the farm. A few of these dairies have additional permits that allow them to sell their milk via retail outlets. They are all regularly inspected and milk samples tested by agriculture regulators.

But in addition, dozens of dairies in Pennsylvania sell raw milk privately via food clubs or herd shares to small groups of consumers. These dairies prefer not to have permits, because Pennsylvania raw dairy permits allow only the sale of fluid milk, and prohibit the sale of other raw dairy products like kefir, yogurt, butter, and ice cream, which many consumers want.

To find dairy options—whether of the permitted or private variety—you can begin by searching on Google, and by asking around. You can call some of the farms listed in the Weston A. Price's realmilk.com [5] web site for suggestions of farmers near to where you live. You can check with friends, or friends of friends.

Raw milk consumers are generally passionate about their food, and are only too glad to help others make the shift, provided they feel you are genuine in your search. A few dairies have been burned by regulators working under cover, posing as consumers, seeking to identify dairies selling raw milk without permits the regulators say are required.

There's also the matter of locating the safest milk supplier possible. I discuss in Chapter 8 ways to evaluate a farm's safety practices.

How much can I expect to pay for raw milk?

It is generally more expensive than what you pay in the supermarket for pasteurized-homogenized milk, sometime by a factor of two or more. So while the processed stuff may sell for $4 or so a gallon, raw milk typically goes for $8 or more a gallon. In California, where raw milk is sold at retail, it sells for $18 a gallon or more. I generally pay from $7.50 to $11 a gallon in the Northeast.

Why is raw milk, which isn't processed at all, so much more expensive than milk that goes through fractionating, pasteurization, and homogenization?

It definitely is counter-intuitive. The explanation for milk is similar as for other products produced on both a manufactured and artisanal basis. As one point of comparison, a mass-produced leather belt might sell for $12, while a hand-crafted leather belt might sell for $30 or $40. A mass-produced wool sweater can be had for $15 or $20, while a hand-knitted sweater might sell for $70 or even $100.Similarly, mass-produced jams and jellies will be cheaper than the hand-made variety.

The reality is that milk intended to be consumed raw is more challenging to produce than milk intended for pasteurization. The main reason has to do with ensuring the raw milk is produced safely, which requires much attention to sanitation. Milk intended for pasteurization has more production latitude, since any pathogens that find their way into the milk will be zapped during pasteurization. Thus, labor costs for raw dairies are likely to be higher than at conventional dairies.

But raw milk is also produced with a focus on milk quality, rather than quantity. Thus, the dairies producing milk for processing are often large dairies, with hundreds or even thousands of cows, which are housed in crowded conditions and fed grain-based diets to keep costs down and increase milk production.

Dairies that produce raw milk keep smaller herds—the largest raw dairy is 400 cows, and most are less than 50 cows. Moreover, the cows are usually kept on pasture (which requires more land than the factory operations), and during the winter provided with expensive hay rather than grain, in the belief that such a diet is more natural for the cows, and leads to more nutritious milk.

How do I locate the lowest priced raw milk?

If you are asking that question with the expectation you can search out inexpensive raw milk, you may not be a good candidate to regularly consume raw milk. I know it's the American way to seek out the lowest-priced food, but for raw milk (and other nutrient-dense foods), price shouldn't be the primary determinant.

In my view, you want the farmer you are buying from to be highly motivated to focus on safety and quality, and not trying to cut corners to keep prices down or reduce quality.

Again in my view, you should want dairy farmers to be able to earn a reasonable living, for the sake of their communities, and to encourage additional small farms. The focus on cutting costs and consolidating farms into ever-larger factory type operations has led to the shutdown of about 90% of America's dairy farms since 1970, according to the U.S. Department of Agriculture. The same trend has led to the shutdown of all varieties of small farms.

Why do farmers want to produce raw milk if it requires so much more attention to sanitation and so much more work to sell it?

Two reasons. First and foremost, the economics are much more attractive. The conventional dairy industry is essentially a cartel—a few corporations and cooperatives control the market, and thus set the prices paid to farmers. Because there is almost no competition among processors to buy milk from dairies, the farmers must take what they are offered for their pre-pasteurized milk, and that price tends to vary between $1.50 to $2.50 a gallon, depending on the commodity market cycle. There are some variations depending on whether the milk is organic, or whether the counts for naturally occurring bacteria are low (higher prices for both these eventualities). The milk is then sold at retail for usually $4 to $5 a gallon.

In the case of raw milk, most is sold by farmers directly to customers, for prices of $8 a gallon and higher. All that money goes directly to the farmers (except when the milk is sold at retail in states allowing retail sales; in that case, the retailer takes about 25% of the price). Thus, we're talking about revenue to farmers triple or more what they receive in the commodity market.

Whereas small dairies of the traditional mode, that sold milk for processing, are increasingly uneconomical, small dairies selling raw milk directly to consumers offer the possibility of making the old traditional small dairy economically viable once again.

The second reason some farmers prefer selling raw milk is that they like having direct contact with their actual customers. In the conventional dairy business, farmers rarely meet the end customer. Raw milk producers often tell me how much satisfaction they get from meeting people who are grateful to be able to access fresh unprocessed milk, and are thrilled because of their improved health. Some farmers hear from parents about how children have gotten rid of asthma and eczema, and feel satisfaction that they are helping supply a product that is doing so much good.

Are you suggesting I stick with a particular farm, or switch around from supplier to supplier?

Generally speaking, I like to encourage regular support of particular farmers. Sometimes it's difficult, though. Because I travel a fair amount, and spend time in a second home, I buy my raw milk through any of three different farmers in New Hampshire and Massachusetts. It's not my ideal, but it works out okay.

You have made reference to farmers getting into trouble with the law. Should I be prepared with a backup supplier in case my farmer gets into trouble?

My feeling is that consumers of raw milk should be prepared to stand behind their farmers if they encounter legal problems with regulators. These problems often have nothing to do with safety. One increasingly common problem is regulators coming after farmers for failure to have retailer or food handling permits. This can be a serious problem in states that have especially restrictive regulations regarding raw milk sales; once the farmer gets a retail license, he or she is then expressly forbidden from selling his or her most popular product, which is raw milk. It is a kind of Catch 22.

So farmers who have food clubs or operate herdshares because their states don't allow retail or on-farm sales of raw milk usually resist such licenses, on the ground the farmers aren't selling to the general public.

When the regulatory problems involve allegations of safety issues, the situation can become more murky. Customers need to assess for themselves if such situations involve genuine safety problems, or what they consider to be exaggerated charges designed to harass. When regulators know that farmers have backing, the regulators are sometimes less inclined to pursue legal cases, with the attendant publicity they bring.

What can customers really accomplish in such situations?

They can accomplish a surprising amount. It is when farmers run into legal problems that they most need the support of their customers. The farmers need the income, and they may need political support. It's much more difficult for regulators to go after hundreds of food club members than to go after a single farmer.

One of the most inspiring examples of how members stuck together to ward off intrusive regulators occurred in Kentucky in 2011. Out of the blue, public health regulators attempted to shut down a food club just before the Memorial Day weekend, by placing a "quarantine" order on the milk that was awaiting member pickup. There was no allegation of a particular safety problem—it's just that Kentucky's laws on raw milk sales weren't entirely clear. The food club's operator, John Moody, contacted members to come as quickly as possible to get their milk, and leave a statement for regulators saying the milk belonged to the members, with the member's phone number if the regulators wanted to call. Needless to say, the regulators backed off and the food club continues to operate.

Chapter 8: How Do I Find the Safest Raw Milk?

If you are new to drinking raw milk, your biggest initial concern is likely to be whether the milk you decide to buy is safe. Unfortunately, you can't tell from looking at or smelling the milk whether or not it contains pathogens. But there are steps you can take to reduce the chances of encountering unsafe milk.

How do I determine in advance if a particular dairy's raw milk is safe?

There are two main things you can do: Check out the dairy's past safety record and check out the dairy's current production practices.

That sounds simple enough, but how do I check these things out?

Checking on a dairy's past safety record is usually the most straightforward task. You can go online and do a Google search of the dairy you are considering buying from.

What if the Google search comes back with a number of links to articles saying the dairy has had to recall milk, or was suspected of making people sick? Do I eliminate the dairy from consideration?

Not necessarily. You need to find out more about exactly what occurred. As I've pointed out in a number of places, regulators have been very tough on raw milk producers, and have in some cases shut down dairies based on questionable circumstances. Even if regulators simply announce an investigation involving a raw dairy, for whatever reason (say, a possible connection to an outbreak of illnesses), that information will be picked up by any of dozens of web sites--generally local media, along with lawyers who specialize in product liability cases, and troll for cases that may lead to recovery of financial damages. The information stays on the Internet forever, even if public health regulators determine during their investigation that the dairy had no connection to a particular outbreak.

How do I spot the truly serious incidents, the real red flags?

That is an important question. The reports you read from your Google search could indicate any number of potential or real problems—that the dairy was shut down because its overall bacterial counts (for non-harmful bacteria) were high, or that pathogens were found in its milk, or that its milk was thought to have made people sick.

For example, several dairies in New York State have been shut down—some repeatedly-- because inspectors said they found *Listeria* in raw milk. It turns out there hasn't been an illness in the U.S. from *Listeria* in raw milk for a decade or more. The reason for at least some of the *Listeria*-related shutdowns seems to be a very tough policy in the U.S. on *Listeria* compared with other parts of the world.

It turns out that just a few cells of *Listeria* don't usually cause illnesses. Indeed, the European Union and Canada have changed their food safety requirements since the late 1990s to allow for up to 100 cells of *Listeria* in a measurement of food, without necessarily taking action against the producer. The FDA operates under a "zero tolerance" standard that requires shutdown if a dairy shows even a single cell of *Listeria* in its milk

Reports of actual illnesses tied to raw milk should be taken seriously, however. Try to determine how regulators made the connection of illnesses to a particular dairy. Were the connections "epidemiological" (meaning they were circumstantial, based on the fact that most or all of the people who became sick had consumed the same food from the same source), or based on genetic matching of pathogens found in victims with pathogens found on a farm?

Are you suggesting there is a difference in attitudes toward food safety in the U.S. versus other nations?

Yes. Other countries, in Europe and Asia, seem more accepting of the reality that any food can make people sick on rare occasions. Thus, we see that raw milk is legal in pretty much every country of Europe, with the exception of Scotland. A number of European countries, like Italy and Slovenia, even allow raw milk vending machines kept full by area farmers. In 2014, the United Kingdom's main food safety agency was considering expanding availability of raw milk beyond only farms.

The likelihood that the Buddha died from tainted pork or mushrooms provided him by an admirer isn't a matter that gets much attention in Asia, where Buddhists are the majority. People tend to be adventuresome in their eating, and not gripped by the fear mongering that prevails in the U.S. over food.

Why the difference in attitudes?

One big reason has to do with the difference in judicial systems. The U.S. is unusual in that its legal system allows individuals who have become sick from tainted food to sue the producer for huge amounts of financial damages. The family of a girl who nearly died back in 1993 from eating tainted hamburger from Jack in the Box received a settlement of $15.6 million. It was the biggest tainted-food settlement ever at that time, and lots more multi-million dollar settlements have followed. Food safety lawyer Bill Marler publicizes that he has obtained more than $600 million of settlements since obtaining that record-setting settlement back in 1993.

Such settlements are unheard of in Europe and Asia.

What else should I be on the lookout for in the event of outbreaks linked to raw milk?

Pay attention to the dairy farmer's response. Is the farmer very defensive? Or is the farmer open to the possibility of his farm's involvement? If the latter, does the farmer express concern about people who may have become ill? Does the farmer keep a list of customers so he or she can alert them if there is a potential safety problem?

In some cases of suspected illnesses, farmers hear directly from people who have become sick, so they often have an early indication about whether their milk was the culprit. If they haven't heard from anyone, that could explain their initial defensiveness. But if they have heard from people who have become ill, and are still in denial, then that could be a tipoff to a non-helpful attitude.

Also pay attention to the farmer's actions. Does he or she order testing on the farm's milk? Does he or she suspend sales while gathering information (though usually, the state will order a suspension pending further testing).

What if the testing comes back negative? Does that mean the farmer's milk had no connection to suspected illnesses?

Not necessarily. Pathogens are usually distributed unevenly in milk, so people can become sick from *Campylobacter* or *E. coli* O157:H7, and milk subsequently tested comes back negative.

This scenario has played out in a number of circumstances involving suspected raw milk illnesses, and it can be maddening.

Are you saying that if pathogens are found in a farm's milk after an outbreak of illnesses, I should avoid that dairy's milk?

Not necessarily. Basically, you need to use your judgment about the situation, along with common sense. How many illnesses were there? How serious were they? Were you able ask around and identify any of the people made ill?

In addition, farmers who have experienced shutdowns or illnesses should be willing to discuss with you their view of what happened. If they are terribly defensive, or don't want to discuss, this should be another red flag. On the other hand, it's a good sign if they are open about what happened, and talk about steps they have taken to correct possible problems.

Are you really suggesting a farmer who has experienced serious illnesses in milk tied to his or her dairy should be allowed to continue selling milk?

In a few cases involving serious illness, the dairies were forced out of business, either because of legal problems following from the outbreak, or because the farmers changed their minds and decided to discontinue producing and selling raw milk. Dairies that shut down after serious illnesses included Dee Creek in Washington in 2006, Town Dairy in Connecticut in 2008, and Foundation Farm in Oregon in 2012.

But some have resolved after illnesses to do better. One example is a dairy in Tennessee, whose raw milk sickened a handful of children with E.coli O157:H7 in 2013. Testing of the farmer's milk by both the farmer and the state failed to turn up the bad bug, but the farmer eventually concluded her cows were producing the unsafe milk. She decided to explore ways to improve safety, and wound up working with the raw milk safety organization, the Raw Milk Institute (RAWMI)--adopting its standards and eventually applying for membership.

A farmer like this, who has learned important lessons from an unfortunate incident like an outbreak of illness, can become even more committed to safe practices than other farmers who haven't had a problem.

What is the Raw Milk Institute?

As I said previously, the Raw Milk Institute (RAWMI) is the first, and thus far only, organization for establishing safety standards for raw milk producers, and for certifying compliance among member farmers. It describes its mission as "to improve human health and the immune system by training and mentoring farmers; educating consumers; establishing national raw milk guidelines; outreach to farmers, consumers, regulators, universities, the media, and other groups; listing producers, and supporting research."

http://rawmilkinstitute.net/about-rawmi/mission-statement/ [1]

How thorough and demanding are its standards?

Its standards are demanding enough that most dairies that apply for certification don't make it through the first time they are up for consideration. It can take some dairies a year or more to fully comply with RAWMI's high standards.

What is your involvement?

I have been a member of RAWMI's Executive Advisory Council since the organization's founding in 2012.

How many certified member dairies does RAWMI have?

As of mid-2014, it had seven members. But applicants have been increasing significantly, and projections are for RAWMI to at least double its membership by the start of 2015.

How did RAWMI get started?

RAWMI was launched by Mark McAfee, owner of Organic Pastures Dairy Co., the nation's largest raw dairy, in California. He was prompted to start RAWMI after two outbreaks associated with his dairy—one in 2006 and another in 2011. He was re-energized by the very serious outbreak of illnesses at Foundation Farm in Oregon in 2012 in which 19 people, many of them children, became sick with E.coli O157:H7. The dairy seemed to have a number of safety issues, and McAfee decided it was time to improve the standards at raw dairy producers everywhere, if raw milk was going to ever gain serious acceptance by public health and agriculture professionals.

What was the premise of its launch?

McAfee feels strongly there is a difference not only between pre-pasteurized raw milk (for processing) and raw milk intended to be sold raw, but among the quality of raw dairies. He says, "We must all end the notion that all raw milk is the same or even similar at all...the new paradigm of thought must be that each source of raw milk has its very own risk profile. In the case of RAWMI listed sources, it appears that these sources are very low risk and consistent in their low-risk profile as well.

"At present...we have ignorant producers selling and producing raw milk to very ignorant and uneducated consumers."

What if I don't see any dairies in my area among RAWMI's members?

That is a challenge. RAWMI is new, and its criteria for approving dairies are very strict. So it has only been able to certify a few dairies in its first two years. As a member of its advisory board, I am glad it has taken a go-slow approach. It needs credibility, and the worst thing that could happen would be for illnesses to develop from dairies that are RAWMI certified.

Are there any commonalities among farms that have had very serious outbreaks of illness?

I have seen two commonalities. First, the people running the raw dairies tend to be inexperienced. They may have come to raw milk with romantic notions of helping people improve their health, but been unprepared for the diligence and systematic hard work essential to produce safe raw milk on a regular basis.

Second, dairies that have transitioned from producing milk for processing may take several years to fully adjust to the new pressure of having to follow tough safety procedures to consistently produce safe milk.

Don't state agriculture departments do continuing education for farmers--"extension" courses--that would cover raw milk safety?

You would think so. But agriculture regulators, like public health regulators, tend to be so skeptical about raw milk that they often try to discourage its production and consumption. In that vein, most agriculture departments and universities long ago discontinued whatever instruction they might have offered to farmers on producing the safest possible raw milk.

That being said, there are indications that extension courses on raw milk may be making a comeback. In

Pennsylvania, Penn State University teamed up with RAWMI to do a day-long seminar on safety practices for raw dairies in late 2014. The University of Maine has also begun listing incorporating raw dairy safety into its extension program. Hopefully these two initiatives will spread.

Is it appropriate for someone like me, who knows little about dairy farming, to be questioning an experienced dairy owner about his or her farming techniques?

Absolutely. In fact, I would argue that you owe it to yourself to ask at least a few basic questions to learn more about how the dairy's milk is produced. And I would argue further that if a farmer puts you off or is snide or condescending in answering, then that amounts to a negative answer, and you may want to cross that dairy off your list of prospective suppliers. Sellers of raw milk know that people are confused about safety. They should be willing to explain how they guard against problems. My personal feeling about a farmer who blows off questions is that the farmer has something to hide, or isn't confident enough about his or her approach to explain it to potential customers.

Are there any "theories" to be on the lookout for?

The big one is a belief among some farmers, and advocates of raw milk, that cows on pasture are immune to producing unsafe milk. This stems from some misleading research that milk coming from cows on grass-only diets naturally contains so much good bacteria, that they overwhelm any pathogens. So be wary of any farmer who says that his or her milk is safe from pathogens because the cows eat only grass. This just isn't true. While cows on pasture are less likely to be exposed to the pathogens that are more likely to crop up among cows crowded together, there have been serious outbreaks involving milk from cows that were eating lots of wonderful grass.

What are the most important questions to ask?

I suggest beginning with this question: What is your experience in dairy farming?

Be especially alert to either of two answers. One suggests they are relatively new to dairy farming, that their dairy farm is the fulfillment of a life-long dream. Ask them to be specific about when they started. If it's less than six years previously, be wary.

Another answer suggests they have been doing dairy farming for many years, maybe even be children or grandchildren of farmers. In that case, they have almost certainly been operating the dairy as a supplier to processors who pasteurized and homogenized the milk. Once again, ask specifically about when they made the transition to selling raw milk. And once again, if it's less than six years previously, be wary.

Why is six years such a significant number?

In my experience, dairies that have had problems with pathogens tend to have either been in operation less than six years, or transitioned from being a conventional dairy fewer than six years earlier. Now, this isn't a hard and fast number. But it basically speaks to the importance of experience in producing safe milk.

What questions might I ask to get insight into training and education a farmer might have in safe raw milk production?

You can inquire about whether the farmer has had any instruction in safe raw milk production. As I said earlier in this chapter, very few university schools of agricultural or state departments of agriculture offer safety instruction for operators of raw dairies. But two other organizations have tried to fill the gap.

The Farm-to-Consumer Legal Defense Fund Foundation , an educational arm of the FTCLDF, commissioned a two-part DVD and guidebook, "Chore Time" [2], about important safety practices for raw dairies. It takes a holistic approach, focusing as much on the cleanliness of equipment as on matters like soil mineralization to ensure cows are eating the most nutritious grass possible to maintain good health. The premise of the farmer providing the instruction, Tim Wightman, is that healthy cows are much less likely to be carrying around pathogens that cause sickness.

The Raw Milk Institute (RAWMI) also provides guidance from its professional dairy experts. Farmers seeking to have their dairies certified by RAWMI are guided through an extensive self evaluation and assessment process before being certified. RAWMI has begun offering day-long workshops for raw milk producers.

So, additional questions to pose to farmers about training are these:

--Have you viewed the Farm-to-Consumer Legal Defense

Fund Foundation's instructions on safety?

--Do you belong to RAWMI?

--If not, do you use RAWMI techniques?

What questions should I ask about the farm's animals?

A key one is this: How does the farm go about adding cows to its herd?

As demand for a dairy's milk grows, it may need to expand the size of its herd to increase production.

The answer you want to hear is that the dairy's cows are a closed herd, meaning the dairy only adds animals naturally, via births by existing cows. The owner of one of the dairies I buy raw milk from always enjoys telling her customers about her cows that have given birth to new calves, which will then be joining the herd.

What if the farm doesn't have a closed herd?

What you really want to know about are major changes to the herd. If the farmer adds cows from outside, try these questions:

-When was the last time you introduced a new animal into the herd?

-Where did you obtain that cow or steer?

Ideally, you want any new cows to come from another organic dairy, or from a farmer that was transitioning out of farming and shutting down to retire, after a successful farming career. The answer you don't want to hear is that the farmer bought the cow at a farm animal auction. This means the cow could have come from anywhere, including a factory farm that fed lots of grains and kept the animal in unhealthy conditions, increasing the likelihood it is carrying around bad bugs.

Are there any other issues I should inquire about?

Here are four other questions to ask:

-Are the cows fed some kind of minerals and/or supplements?

-Is there hot running water for both cleaning equipment and handwashing?

-Can you segregate sick cows from the rest of the lactating herd?

-Do you have ways to keep your chickens apart from your cows being milked (because *Campylobacter* has become so widespread among chickens)?

Ideally, you want to hear positive answers to these questions. Keep in mind, if you regularly visit a particular farm and talk with the farmer, you will learn about other issues of importance to the farmer, for which there aren't necessarily clear-cut answers. For example, you may learn the farmer keeps the calves with the mother cows for some weeks or even months, to replicate nature's way. Or you may learn that the farmer immediately separates calves from their mothers, to avoid the shock of having to separate them later, and to reduce the chances of the spread of E.coli

0157:H7 (which is more prevalent in calves than cows).

Should I ask the farmer whether the state tests the farm's milk?

Yes, in those states that allow on-farm sales, there is usually a state-sponsored testing program. While you can usually find information via a Google search, it's useful to ask the farmer as well, since the state testing programs tend to shift over time. Some test on a monthly basis, while some test on a quarterly basis. Some test for pathogens, while others just test for a few serious but rare diseases like brucellosis or tuberculosis. Some test for coliforms while other don't, and just focus on standard plate counts.

Should I inquire about whether the farmer does his or her own regular testing of its milk?

Yes. This question is especially relevant if you are dealing with a farm that provides milk via a herd share or cow share, and doesn't come under state licensing regulations. More raw dairies today are doing regular testing of their milk. Mostly, this involves sending samples to certified labs to check for pathogens and counts of non-pathogenic bacteria.

Do any raw dairies do their own testing?

As equipment costs have come down, more dairies are have moved to doing their own testing, even if their own state has a testing program. One farmer who has become an advocate of on-farm testing is Ed Shank, owner of The Family Cow dairy in Pennsylvania (and a member of

RAWMI). His farm's milk is tested by the state, but he has decided he wants to have more frequent and up-to-date testing of his own. Here is what he has to say about what he refers to as "pre-distribution testing":

"It's neither difficult nor highly technical to learn to run coliform and SPC (standard plate count) tests accurately on farm. I've mentored several raw milk farmers through the testing and reading steps of their first samples. They all got the hang of it very quickly."

He adds, "The lab set-up cost is extremely affordable (under $500 if you skip the optional light box and magnifier). When we first set up The Family Cow laboratory, we consulted with microbiologists at Pennsylvania Department of Agriculture (PDA) and two other state certified laboratories. The technicians there advised us what to purchase and also provided the initial mentoring on the correct testing and test reading methodology."

His conclusion: "Running a test-and-hold on-farm laboratory is so easy, so economical and does so much to reduce raw milk risk that it is a no brainer no matter how small the raw milk farm...We have been using our lab for two years now and would never ever go back. Once you get used to pre-consumptive testing on every single lot, post-consumptive testing feels all wrong. Other farmers that I've taught report the same. All are totally delighted with how their lab improves their milking performance, milk quality, the level of food safety reassurance that they now offer their families and peace of mind for everyone all around."

Assuming the farmer does do testing, what should I want to know, besides the fact that there have been no pathogens found?

You can ask to see the results of tests from the previous couple months. Hopefully, the farmer has that data easily available, and extracted from all the small print of the actual report. Best case (and this is beginning to happen), the farmers are posting such data on their farm web sites.

You should primarily be focused on:

-Coliform count: you want this ideally to be 10 or under.

-Standard plate count (SPC): you want this ideally to be under 10,000.

These on-farm tests don't usually involve testing for actual pathogens. Such tests, even in labs, aren't necessarily reliable; as I mentioned earlier in this chapter, people can get sick from pathogens that show up unevenly in milk, and thus aren't necessarily captured in tests.

The bacteria that dairies self-test for are indicators of sanitation or disease problems. Thus, low coliform and SPC are indicative of healthy animals in clean surroundings producing safe milk.

What if there are readings above these numbers?

Ask the farmer why there seem to have been spikes. Perhaps one sick cow drove the numbers up, and that cow has been pulled from the herd, or has recovered. Or perhaps a friend did the milking for a week, and didn't know all the processes. If the spikes seem to be occurring fairly often, that may be a sign to be wary.

Can I reasonably assume that on-farm testing represents assurance my family and I won't get sick from the milk?

No. Testing is simply another risk-reduction tool. Favorable results reduce the odds of there being pathogens in the milk. Testing doesn't eliminate the odds of illness altogether.

In the case of the testing Ed Shank was describing in answer to a previous question, the results mainly provide an indication about farm cleanliness. Coliforms and standard plate count are indicators of cleanliness and animal health—the lower the counts, the better. But no test, even for particular pathogens in the milk, will provide a guarantee. The testing just isn't sophisticated or complete enough.

Are there any indications in terms of appearance or smell of a dairy farm that are tip-offs about safety?

Be concerned if a barn smells heavily of manure, rather than just faintly.

Also observe the cows' appearance. Are they clean or are their legs and thighs coated in mud or manure? Mud and manure can be signs of less than optimal cleanliness.

Cows can shed E.coli 0157:H7 when there is stress of different kinds, like less than optimal cleanliness or changing diets. Be aware that cows shed more E.coli in the spring, because of the stress associated with going back to pasture. Locales with intense late-summer heat can also be stressors.

Are there any tip-offs in terms of the taste or smell of the milk I should be on the lookout for?

I would say that if your fresh raw milk tastes funny or "off," I would not drink it, and I would alert the farmer.

I would also be alert to smells of sourness, from the milk "turning," after just a few days. Raw milk should keep for at least ten days, even two weeks or more, before beginning to smell. If raw milk begins giving off a sour or spoiled smell after just three or four days, that is a sign it left the dairy with higher numbers of coliforms, or other spoilage bacteria, which are harmless bacteria, but can signify sanitation issues at a dairy. Or it could be that the milk wasn't properly refrigerated; keeping the cold chain from farm to home is important in maintaining milk quality. (Always bring a cooler when picking up raw milk from a farm or drop site.)

In any event, I would alert the dairy if milk shows signs of spoilage in just a few days. If the owner makes light of it ("just nature's way," for example), and it keeps happening, I would think about switching raw milk suppliers.

Should I inquire about whether a farm has liability insurance to cover damages if people get sick?

You can certainly inquire. Many farms that have state permits to sell raw milk will have liability insurance. But farms that are organized as herd shares or private food clubs likely won't have insurance. Insurance companies have tightened their underwriting standards so as to restrict availability of insurance to producers of raw milk. Opponents of raw milk have publicly encouraged insurance companies to restrict insurance availability, as a way to reduce the availability of raw milk.

In general, I'd suggest you make your decision about purchasing raw milk from a particular supplier based on other criteria I have discussed related to safety, rather than whether the provider has insurance. But as with other issues related to your assessment, the weight you give to insurance is a personal matter.

This may sound crazy, but what about buying my own cow and producing my own milk. Is that something that is realistic?

Believe it or not, there are many dozens, probably many hundreds of people, around the country who have done just that. They have acquired one or two cows to ensure their own personal supply of raw milk, under their own control.

I know of one couple in suburban Philadelphia that bought a single cow a few years ago from an Amish farm, and they are happily enjoying the milk. Indeed, the cow gives more milk than they can drink each day, so they have taken to making cheeses, butter, and ice cream. They also give some to a few neighbors who have requested it.

As great as it sounds, there are some challenges to this kind of arrangement. One big one is a cow's space requirements. You need a building that can serve as a barn, for milking and shelter. You also need enough land for the cow to eat pasture during the warm months.

Another challenge is committing to being available for milking the cow once or twice a day, 365 days a year. This makes it tough to get away on vacations, or even for weekends, without help from friends or relatives to fill in.

It's more than taking care of a pet like a cat or dog, since the helpers need to know how to milk and otherwise care for a cow and the milk. And finally, cows are social animals, and keeping a single cow can make for a lonely cow, at least until she has a calf.

The owners of so-called family cows tend to network with each other for tips and ideas about how to best care for their new farm animals. They tend to find each other via any of several raw milk listserves and conferences on sustainable food, or Google "family cow" and review advice from owners and other experts.

Chapter 9: How Do I Find the Best Quality Raw Milk?

Once you have located possible sources, and assured yourself about their safety, you can think more about the real fun stuff—comparing milk sources and finding the milk you like best. Unlike pasteurized milk, raw milk can differ widely from farm to farm in taste and fat content.

It could be you don't have a lot of choices. It may be you are in a state without many raw milk producers, and are only able to find one source both convenient to access and whose safety practices you feel comfortable with.

Most dairies that are committed to producing and selling raw milk are proud of the quality of their milk. Some are partial to certain breeds of cows they feel produce the best quality milk. Some are committed to milking their cows only once a day, in the belief that, while this reduces productivity over what it would be if they followed the standard twice-a-day milking regimen, improves the butterfat content, and thus the quality.

How do you define "the best" raw milk?

This is in many respects a personal matter. Just as we each define "the best" wine or coffee or cantaloupe differently, so is it with raw milk.

The notion that milk varies in quality takes a little getting used to. The pasteurized variety most of us have been drinking for many years is notable mostly for its sameness—it doesn't vary in taste or appearance, no matter the location, the time of year, or other variables.

People tend to define raw milk quality by its creaminess. Some raw milk just has more cream than others—the amount generally varies from 4% to 6% (versus a maximum of 3.5% in pasteurized whole milk available in supermarkets). Those tend to be the ones that make us lick our chops and say, "This is like ice cream."

But raw milk can vary in taste, as well. Some raw milk has a sweet taste.

There can also be seasonal variations that affect appearance. During the late spring and summer, cows eating from lush fresh pasture in the Northeast and Midwest will give milk that has a slightly yellow hue to the cream—this is due to a high beta-carotene content, a fat-soluble vitamin plentiful in carrots and dark leafy greens.

Which cows give the best milk?

Once again, you are talking a lot about personal tastes. Veteran raw milk drinkers tend to prefer milk with the highest butterfat content, because the fat gives the milk it's creamy, almost ice-cream-like texture.

Do cow breeds vary according to butterfat content?

Yes, according to farmers. Not surprisingly, most farmers say the breed they own gives the best milk. I've heard this from farmers raising Ayshires, Jerseys, Guernseys, and Devonshires. Some farmers (raising Jerseys) say Jerseys have the highest fat content. Others say milk from Devonshires have the most conjugated linoleic acids (CLA) of any milk products (CLA is thought to confer health benefits). I've had milk from each of these breeds, and have enjoyed the milk from all. My own personal preference is the milk from Guernseys raised by a New Hampshire farmer I have long purchased milk from.

You didn't mention Holsteins. Do they give good milk?

Interesting about Holsteins—they comprise about 90% of all cows on American dairy farms, yet I've never met a raw milk farmer who raises mainly Holsteins. The knock on Holsteins is that they have been bred to produce the highest volume of milk of any breed, but that high production comes at the price of lower butterfat than other breeds.

So while a Jersey might give three to five gallons daily, a Holstein on a commercial factory-style dairy might be turning out as much as eight gallons daily.

Can I get low-fat or skim raw milk?

Low-fat or skim raw milk is generally only available from large dairies that sell their raw milk via retail outlets. Your average small dairy won't bother with skim or low fat because most raw milk drinkers want full-fat milk, since the fat is thought to be especially nutritious, helping people absorb vitamins and other nutrients more fully.

Keep in mind that it is possible to make your own skim milk simply by removing the cream that rises to the top of all non-homogenized milk. (After all, "skim" milk is simply milk that has had the cream skimmed off.) You can then use the cream to make butter or whipped cream or put it into your coffee.

Is there an easy way to determine the butterfat content of a particular container of milk?

The best way I know of is to look at the "cream line"—where the cream ends and the remaining milk begins, after the milk has sat a few hours. The cream line in milk with a very high butterfat content may well reach one-fourth of the way or more down the container. Milk with lower butterfat content may only extend one-eighth of the way down the container.

What's the deal if the cream line doesn't go down very far? Is that a function of the breed or does it mean the farmer is skimming some of the cream to make butter?

It could stem from either of the causes you mention. Or it could be a result of seasonal fluctuations, with more cream being produced during the summer when the cows are on grass versus the winter when they are eating hay. If the cream line seems meager, you might inquire with the farmer especially if the cream line is much higher than you saw in milk from other dairies, or higher than other milk from the same dairy.

Doesn't raw milk have a short shelf life?

Not necessarily. Raw milk that isn't produced under the most sanitary conditions can leave the dairy with high numbers of spoilage-type bacteria that lead to smelly milk within just a few days. However, milk that leaves the dairy with low number of such bacteria may last two or three weeks without smelling sour.

It's important to appreciate that raw milk and pasteurized milk age differently. As Ted Beals, the retired Michigan pathologist, explains, when raw milk exceeds its "shelf-life" it clabbers (a natural and healthy change). Some of the consumers of fresh milk deliberately allow this change to happen by taking their milk out of the refrigerator, because they like the changed texture and altered nutrition.

When pasteurized milk exceeds its shelf-life it "spoils"(a degenerative process affecting the quality of the product and making it smell, taste, and look bad, and thus making it unmarketable). Note: drinking either types of milk that have undergone these changes will NOT cause a person to become sick!

A few years ago, I read about a controversy over something known as "A1 vs. A2 milk". What is that all about?

It's a little out there, even for raw milk. In 2009, an Australian researcher wrote a book that got a lot of public attention: *Devil in the Milk: Illness, Health and the Politics of A1 and A2 Milk*. The book argued that milk from older breeds, like Jersey cows, is healthier than milk from newer breeds, like Holsteins. Moreover, the newer-breed milk, or A1, might be unhealthy, encouraging heart disease, type 2 diabetes, and autism, he asserted. The author, Keith Woodford, based his argument on a genetic mutation that he contended occurred many years ago and adversely affected the newer breeds.

For a while, raw milk drinkers were avidly inquiring with farmers whether their cows were producing A1 or A2 milk. Those dairies with A2 cows saw their sales soar.

The controversy has died down some in recent years as it has become apparent that there are likely any number of factors in milk that affect its overall nutrition and health benefits, and that the A1/A2 issue is just one such factor, and possibly a minor factor. Still, some dairy farmers continue to test their herds as to whether they are A1 or A2 (or a combination), and to breed their cows as much as possible toward A2 producers.

There is nothing wrong with inquiring with farms you are considering buying milk from about their herd's composition.

How can I find other experienced raw milk drinkers to talk with about their recommendations for finding the best raw milk, who won't be proselytizing?

One way to get introduced to others is to find your local chapter of the Weston A. Price Foundation [1]. It's the leading advocate organization about raw milk; while at first glance it seems as if it might be a source of proselytizing, it turns out that many of the people involved are ordinary people from all walks of life.

Chapter 10: Bringing Raw Milk Into Your Home... Peacefully

Family food decisions are becoming ever more complicated. Should we go vegetarian? Limited vegetarian? Paleo? Can some members of the family be vegetarian and others be Paleo (sometimes referred to as "the caveman diet" because of its emphasis on proteins and de-emphasis of carbs)?

As people become more sophisticated about food, and educated about its potential benefits and dangers, more of these kinds of decisions are being debated in family kitchens.

Increasingly, these decisions get tangled up in other related issues, like food costs, effects on the environment, animal rights...and perceived risk, or safety. This latter issue is often front and center as families debate whether or not to include raw milk as part of the family diet.

As it so often does in public health circles, raw milk seems to raise emotions in family matters as well. In Maine, a big controversy [1] broke out in 2013 when a mother's doctor objected to her feeding her infant child a formula based on goat milk. The doctor got human services involved, and for a while, there was uncertainty about whether the mother might lose custody of her child. Word got out on social media, and soon there were public demonstrations outside the doctor's medical center, along with intense discussion on blogs and Facebook; eventually the state authorities backed off.

Mark McAfee of Organic Pastures Dairy Co. says he has been contacted by a number of parents seeking his input on threats in divorce or custody situations to use the presence of raw milk in a home to suggest a parent is reckless. He recalls in 2014 receiving a call from a single mom distressed because the baby's father "wanted custody of their 17-month-old daughter and was using the 'warning' label on the back of our OPDC milk bottle as an example of unfit mothering!!!" The father was also citing raw-milk warnings from the FDA and the American Academy of Pediatrics against the mother. He says he urged the mom to fight back with positives about raw milk, and it's not clear how the case was resolved.

In my judgment, such cases aren't to be taken lightly. They represent strong feelings and provide further evidence of just how controversial raw milk has become in our society.

When I told my husband I wanted to substitute raw milk for pasteurized milk in our family, he nearly threatened to divorce me. How do I deal with that kind of opposition?

That is probably the most difficult question in this entire book There is no easy or simple solution to this kind of problem, except for me to say that while it isn't unusual, it is solvable. It's something that is best resolved via discussion and compromise rather than via ultimatums and threats.

Part of the resolution depends on where you and your family stand in terms of your overall approach to food. I'd suggest, especially if you are looking to raw milk to help resolve particular medical or health issues, that you stand back and try to gain a broader perspective.

What do you mean by a broader perspective?

To begin with, it's helpful if you can come up with an overall philosophy about your food values. Here are a few questions to ask yourselves:

-Do you believe food is food is food....in other words, that all foods are pretty much the same in nutritional benefit, whether from a factory farm or small local farm, organic vs conventional?

-Do you avoid artificial sweeteners?

-Do you avoid GMO foods?

-Do you try to avoid eating meats that may have been raised on antibiotics?

-Do you shop for food based mostly on price (seeking biggest bargains)?

-Do you value locally-grown food?

How does raw milk fit into this discussion?

My experience in informing people about raw milk is that people who have come to believe in the importance of a healthy lifestyle will be those most interested in raw milk. They are concerned about the dangers of artificial sweeteners, GMO foods, antibiotic residues in meats, excessive processing, and believe that local and organic foods are healthiest.

These concerns and the various books (like The Omnivore's Dilemma) and documentaries (like "Food Inc") on food production help explain the explosive growth of organic food, and of the retail grocery chain, Whole Foods, over the past thirty-plus years. Whole Foods has grown from a single store in Austin, Texas to 360 around the U.S. by 2014.

A Gallup Poll [2] taken in 2014 showed that 45% of all Americans seek out organic foods. Clearly, many Americans have shifted in their attitudes on food.

Are you suggesting that people shouldn't make a shift to introducing raw milk into their diets without looking at some of the other issues you list?

Yes, I have come to feel strongly that raw milk isn't something people can adopt in isolation. How one reacts to the idea of paying double or triple the supermarket price for milk becomes part of a larger question about whether you trust the food system, and how important food is to you.

I always think about the old saw that there are people who eat to live and those who live to eat. People who eat to live tend not to be intrigued by raw milk. In their view, all food is much the same, all spinach or butter or eggs are pretty much the same in nutritional benefit, whether from a factory farm or small local farm, organic vs. conventional.

People who live to eat often adopt a more involved food philosophy. It may be completely vegetarian, or it may be vegetarian with dairy and eggs, or it may be the Weston A. Price Foundation philosophy of lots of nutrient-dense food based heavily on animal fat and protein from animals raised on pasture. People who commit to raw milk often do so as part of a nutrient-dense orientation in which they seek out fat-rich proteins, including not only milk but animal organs, eggs, fermented foods, and lots of beef. The foods may or may not be served raw.

I have a couple friends who know about my interest in raw milk and have inquired as to whether I would recommend it for them. I happen to know these individuals are in the "eat to live" category, and so I've advised them it's probably not right for them, that they should come back to it once they've made a larger shift in their attitudes on food.

So, let's say my spouse and I have this discussion you suggest, and it turns out we are in agreement philosophically about the importance of eating good food, but my spouse is still opposed to raw milk because of the perceived risk?

My feeling is that a spouse's concerns about risk deserve respect (as do any number of concerns that can come up among couples). Often the best way to resolve such disagreements in philosophy is to compromise.

How can you compromise on raw milk? Either you serve it or you don't.

I admit it does sound far-fetched to speak of compromise over raw milk. But there are ways to be flexible. Here are three options, from most to least favorable to the raw milk advocate in the family:

1. Introduce raw milk very gradually. Begin by limiting raw milk to parents. Then, after some weeks or months, as they find they aren't getting sick, gradually introduce it to the children. Or, introduce it to everyone in tiny increments, an ounce a day the first couple days, then increased to two

ounces, and so on.

2. Limit your family's use of raw milk products to particular products, like raw milk kefir, yogurt, and butter, and avoid fluid raw milk entirely. Kefir is a fermented product, and thus less likely than raw milk to contain pathogens. In fact, there are very few reported cases of illness from raw milk kefir—I have only heard of one over the last decade, and it wasn't a serious illness. And once again, begin by introducing the kefir very gradually. The challenge with kefir is that children, in particular, tend not to like its sour taste as much as they do fresh milk, and thus will consume less. But, mixed with fruit and/or honey, or better yet, made into a smoothie with fruit and honey and spinach leaves, it can become more enticing, and very nutritious.

3. Avoid raw milk products entirely, and seek out locally-produced minimally pasteurized and non-homogenized milk. That way, you get the benefits of milk from cows that are likely on pasture, and raised humanely. The Weston A. Price Foundation recommends this approach when raw milk isn't easily available. To make up for the "good" bacteria you're not getting from raw dairy products, introduce high-quality pasteurized kefir and yogurt, along with commercial probiotics into everyone's diet—available in powder or capsule form from quality suppliers of nutritional supplements.

What if there is an urgent health problem that I think could be helped with raw milk, but my spouse is opposed?

This is an increasingly common difficulty. It may be that a

child has been experiencing chronic ongoing eczema that is not only upsetting the child, but interfering with everyone's sleep, and both parents are frustrated. A pediatrician is suggesting steroid-based drugs. Mom is afraid of the possible side effects of such powerful drugs and wants to try raw milk first, while Dad wants to "go with the experts," and avoid the risks of raw milk.

Is compromise possible? I think so. Possibly Mom decides go along with the steroids for some limited amount of time, say a month or two. If they don't help the eczema and/or cause bad side effects, the parents might then try raw milk, and give that a few months. Sometimes, if there are positive effects from the milk, the opposing parent's views soften.

Let's say the desire by one family member to introduce raw milk is less specific—it stems from concern about overall family health, that family members have been having frequent colds and flu. How does the family resolve the intense opposition to raw milk by one parent, or other family member?

Sometimes the disagreement can be resolved by having everyone do their own thing. In my family, I buy raw milk for myself, and my wife abstains.

As I suggested previously, the big challenge comes when there are little children, and one parent wants to serve them raw milk and the other is opposed.

Or it may be that the parents try raw milk first for a few months, to confirm that the product is safe, and then begin introducing it to children on a very gradual basis.

If the opposition by one parent is absolute, however,

my personal view is to respect the wishes of the opposing spouse, and not try to force raw milk into the family. Otherwise, if there is ever a health problem that seems to stem from the milk, even a minor problem, there could be huge conflict ("I told ya so!")

If I decide not to feed raw milk to my children, what would be other possible options for getting the benefits of raw milk?

As I mentioned previously, kefir or yogurt made from raw milk can be good options. There are very few examples over many years of any illnesses from these products, probably because they are fermented and thus have large amounts of "good" bacteria.

Some raw milk producers also make kefir and yogurt. (Some are prohibited under state regulations that allow raw milk production, but prohibit production of any "processed" dairy products.) You can find a number of instructional videos about making kefir and yogurt at YouTube—just search under "raw milk kefir" or "raw milk yogurt."

Raw milk cheese has its own set of "good" bacteria, if, indeed, it is truly raw. Some cheese labeled as "raw" is heated past 140 degrees, and thus can be considered pasteurized, in the view of some purists. Another challenge is that children tend not to have developed the tastes to appreciate, or even like, raw milk cheese...certainly not as much as they usually take to milk of any kind.

Couldn't I just buy raw milk and pasteurize it myself?

Yes, that is certainly possible. You would need to heat it

to 140 degrees, and keep it there for at least 30 minutes.

Doing that, you would certainly be obtaining high-quality milk from a known source, and dealing with your worries about drinking it raw. You would also be keeping it unhomogenized. But you would be neutralizing what many people consider to be the milk's greatest assets: its rawness and the proteins, enzymes, and good bacteria that are part of that.

Moreover, pasteurizing it yourself probably isn't the best way to ensure yourself the most consistent pasteurizing. If you are determined to drink pasteurized milk, I'd be inclined to obtain it from one of the increasing numbers of small dairies now specializing in producing minimally pasteurized milk, usually non-homogenized. These dairies use equipment made specifically to pasteurize milk at the requisite temperature for the requisite time.

Okay, this is going to sound a bit condescending....but the raw milk drinkers I see quoted in the media seem to be libertarians or Tea Party types, and that isn't me. Am I an oddball to be thinking seriously about raw milk?

The media has definitely tried to portray raw milk drinkers as politically or religiously extreme. The magazine *Mother Jones*, in a 2012 article [3] suggesting that raw milk poses a serious health hazard, said that "fans of raw milk...tend to defend the stuff with near-religious fervor..." *The New Yorker* magazine, also in a 2012 article [4] about regulatory conflicts over raw milk, said, "Suspicion of technology has long been associated with the raw-milk movement."

My experience in going to a wide variety of food-related

conferences and rallies on behalf of raw milk producers being prosecuted is that raw milk drinkers come from all walks of life. Some are young, some are older. Some are teachers and some are in law enforcement and even politics. Massachusetts' former Gov. Duval Patrick is understood to be a long-time raw milk drinker. Some are even physicians, who prescribe it to their patients.

But when I mentioned to a good friend that I was seriously considering serving raw milk to my children, she gave me such a look, and asked, "Isn't that supposed to be very dangerous?" How do I respond to the disapproval of others?

Well, you could begin by recommending your friend buy this book. ☺ But beyond that, I'd suggest responding non-emotionally and matter-of-factly—perhaps to the effect, "I have done a lot of investigating, and that's not what I have found. But, yes, there are people who have that opinion."

I have found that it's usually best not to initiate conversations or provide unsolicited advice about raw milk to people you know, whose food preferences and biases you aren't sure about. You may be all excited because you have found a great food, and have begun to enjoy it, but many people have the kinds of prejudices referred to in the above question....plus other prejudices as well.

What about telling our pediatrician?

I would generally avoid discussing your raw milk inclinations with any professional medical people, unless you know they are open-minded about it. I hate to generalize, but in my experience, pediatricians know little about raw milk, and so when asked, they revert to what they were taught in medical school, that raw milk is terribly dangerous. If they bother to check further, their prejudices tend to be reinforced by the nearly virulent opposition to raw milk expressed repeatedly by the American Academy of Pediatrics. In late 2013, it came out with an especially strident policy statement [5] opposing raw milk—in addition to repeating previous comments it had made saying raw milk was dangerous, this time it said it wanted to see individual states take steps to ban raw milk.

Aren't there any medical professionals who might be sympathetic to raw milk?

Yes, a small but rapidly growing number of medical professionals are now partial to raw milk. Physicians scattered around the country have become backers of raw milk as they have seen its positive health effects on their patients.

By far the largest group of raw milk health-care supporters are alternative care providers—naturopaths, chiropractors, and osteopaths. Some even buy raw milk in quantity from farmers and keep it on hand to make available for particular patients whom the health care professionals judge could benefit from it.

What if I am in the "live to eat" category, but I am shifting from a vegetarian to a dairy-meat diet because of a desire for more protein and fat. How do I best get started on raw milk?

A good way to get started is with kefir, which is easier to digest and consume than raw milk. Raw kefir can be effervescent and has a sour or tangy taste. As noted earlier in this chapter, one way to deal with the tangy taste is to use it to make fruit smoothies. I find frozen bananas and strawberries good fruits to mix in, to get a nice thick consistency. If you can't buy kefir from a farmer, you can make it yourself by obtaining a starter culture and letting it sit at room temperature in milk; there is a fair amount of advice available on YouTube instructional videos.

Once again, it's advisable to start slowly, with small portions, to test out your digestive system. It's possible that all the new bacteria and enzymes could create some initial stomach upset. So go gradual, give yourself a week on kefir and kefir smoothies. You may begin to notice that your digestion improves, that your system actually appreciates the new addition.

Once you've gotten used to kefir, you can begin adding a few ounces of raw milk each day for another week or so, gradually acclimating your system to this new food source.

Let's say I have my family on board and we become regular raw milk drinkers. What do I do about serving raw milk to my children's friends?

Don't do it, at least without inquiring with the parents of your children's friends as to whether it is okay with them. Unfortunately, in this day and age, when there is so much sensitivity to and about food, it's important to inquire with parents about serving all kinds of foods. For example, some families are on vegan diets, and parents don't want their children having meat. Some parents don't want their children having any sugary snacks. Indeed, allergies from nuts are rampant among children, so you shouldn't even serve something as simple as peanut butter without inquiring first.

Are there any other things I should know as I contemplate a switch to raw milk and other nutrient-dense foods?

Unless you are one of the fortunate few who live in a state that allows retail sales of raw milk, and also lives near a retail outlet that carries it, you need to be willing to commit more time and energy to obtaining your food than you have been accustomed to. In most places, you either have to travel to the farm to obtain raw milk, along with other foods like cheeses, eggs and meats that most dairy farmers have available...or you must be willing to travel to a drop site (like a neighbor's garage or patio) at particular times to pick up your food. Even if you belong to a food club, and share responsibility for obtaining food, you may have to make the farm trip every few weeks. And you'll need to plan your orders a few days in advance.

What is your view of the future of raw milk?

I tend to be an optimist about the marketplace. Products that provide significant benefits usually win out in the end, even if there are significant forces arrayed against them. Makers of buggy whips and horse-drawn carriages pushed hard against automobiles. Producers of margarine warned for years about the safety of butter, until margarine was found to have its own health problems, and eventually faded away, while butter has surged in popularity.

The conventional dairy industry detests raw milk, out of fear that raw milk will continue to grab more market share. So the industry will likely continue fighting hard against raw milk, and encouraging the public health profession to keep up the fight. But as more people experience health benefits, and dairy farmers discover that raw milk can be a more profitable product than conventional milk, the marketplace for raw milk will inevitably expand, and people will demand easier access.

Do you have any parting words of advice?

Know that if you do head down the raw milk path, it will almost certainly become part-and-parcel of an exciting journey in which you will become more knowledgeable about your food choices and more intimately engaged with the suppliers of your food. If you join a food club or herd share, you may well find yourself in a new, and exciting, community of people you can share with and learn from. Moreover, the journey will likely lead you into questions about the sources and handling of all your food. You may well consider producing some of your own food. After all, you are what you eat and drink.

Resources

The Complete Patient

http://www.thecompletepatient.com

This blog that I host has become a gathering place for people interested in raw milk, ranging from dairy farmers to consumers to government regulators. I report on and analyze studies and trends affecting raw milk, usually taking a pro-choice approach. The commentary following my posts is often more informative to readers than what I write.

Farm-to-Consumer Legal Defense Fund

http://www.farmtoconsumer.org

Founded on July 4, 2007, it has represented most of the raw dairy producers around the country who have been confronted with legal actions over raw milk and other issues by state and federal food regulatory agencies. Thus, its web site is full of information about the legal arguments in various cases. Its web site also contains a very useful interactive map that provides information on each state's regulations concerning raw milk.

Farm-to-Consumer Legal Defense Fund Foundation

http://f2cfnd.org/resources/#chore%20time

This offshoot of the Farm-to-Consumer Legal Defense Fund provides a variety of resources to farmer and consumers. One of its most important is a collection of safety guides for farmers and consumers. These include a book and two videos advising on safe milking, packaging, and related practices, developed by dairy consultant Tim Wightman. Free.

FarmMatch

http://www.farmmatch.com

FarmMatch is a web site that seeks to connect consumers with farmers, food clubs, and farmers markets, and is the brainchild of food rights activist Max Kane. Consumers who join (no charge) can quickly see what farms and other food outlets in their areas are selling what particular kinds of vegetables, meats, and dairy products, including raw milk.

Food Safety News

http://www.foodsafetynews.com

This publication is a chronicler of food-borne illness, mainly in the U.S. Reflecting the interests of its owner, food safety lawyer Bill Marler, FSN also provides coverage of regulations and illnesses involving raw milk, usually from a negative slant. Just search "raw milk" from its home page.

Mercola.com

http://rawmilk.mercola.com

Osteopathic physician Dr. Joseph Mercola runs the largest natural health web site, and part of the site is devoted to providing information about raw milk. Dr. Mercola is an advocate of raw milk, and advises consumers to use it to improve their health.

Raw Milk Institute (RAWMI)

http://rawmilkinstitute.net

This fledgling organization holds its raw milk producers around the country to a set of tough standards for production and sanitation. On its web site, it posts the results of testing done of its members for naturally occurring bacteria that are indicative of cleanliness and good animal health. RAWMI also has begun offering day-long courses for dairy farmers in producing the safest possible raw milk.

Real Raw Milk Facts

http://www.realrawmilkfacts.com

Launched by food safety lawyer Bill Marler as an anti-raw-milk site, it has accumulated data unavailable elsewhere, about research involving safety and nutrition. It has data drawn from the CDC and other sources on illnesses from raw milk, as well as a variety of research papers.

U.S. Centers for Disease Control and Prevention

http://www.cdc.gov/foodsafety/rawmilk/raw-milk-index.html

This government agency, charged with disseminating education information and maintaining American public health, has taken the position that raw milk is inherently unsafe, and thus must be discouraged as much as possible. All the research and related info it provides is guided by that premise.

Its scientists feel so strongly about it that raw milk is the only food to have earned a CDC web site. It includes several videos from victims and parents of victims of raw milk illnesses.

Weston A. Price Foundation

http://www.realmilk.com

This pro-raw-milk organization hosts the realmilk web site, with its listings of state regulations, and the names of farms that sell raw milk. It should be noted that a number of farms have had their listings pulled, for fear of being harassed by government regulators.

Acknowledgments

I've been very fortunate in my research on raw milk to have access to a wonderful community support system. I've learned the ins and outs of raw milk from highly committed and knowledgeable people who are involved with it on a daily basis—dairy farmers, consumer activists, lawyers, scientists, regulators, medical professionals, and others.

I've met many of them via my blog, The Complete Patient (www.thecompletepatient.com), which I launched in 2006 to report on issues around holistic health. It morphed into a site reporting on emerging controversies over food rights and choice, with the primary one being access to raw milk.

It is their commitment to not only advancing accessibility, but also to ensuring the quality and safety of raw milk that gives me hope that ever more people will have the option to choose for themselves something as basic as what kind of milk to serve their families. Most of all, this community is committed to making sure the public is informed about it food options, including the pros and cons of different choices.

As evidence of the commitment, more than 100 of them stepped up to offer financial support of this book via a crowd funding campaign I hosted in February 2015. They wanted to make sure this book had the resources to reach as wide an audience as possible, so as to counter government and industry misinformation efforts aimed at placing severe limits on, or even banning, raw milk. These supporters included Deborah Freedman, Gramen Farm of Houston, Mark Grieshop, Joel Hall, and Organic Pastures Dairy Co.

The fact that I have access to such a wonderful community doesn't mean we agree on everything.

Indicative of the many questions that surround the raw milk controversy, we often disagree.

I hesitate to try and name all the people I have learned from, since I am sure to leave out some important individuals. A partial list incudes California dairy farmer Shawna Barr, Raw Milk Institute veterinarian and board member Catharina Berge, Weston A. Price Foundation founder and president Sally Fallon, soil and organic farming expert Joseph Heckman of Rutgers University, food safety researcher Michele Jay-Russell of the University of California/Davis, Pete Kennedy and Gary Cox of the Farm-to-Consumer Legal Defense Fund, naturopath Rosanne Lindsay, Mark McAfee of the Raw Milk Institute, food rights activists Liz Reitzig and Sally O'Boyle of the Nourishing Liberty blog, Maine farmer and activist Heather Retberg, Virginia farmer and author Joel Salatin, Canadian activists and farmers Michael Schmidt and Montana Jones, food safety lawyer Bill Marler, activist mom Mary McGonigle-Martin, activist Judith McGeary, and Pennsylvania raw dairy producer Edwin Shank.

I want to acknowledge as well the important help I've received in producing this book from editorial professionals passionate about food—proofreaders Sharon Zecchinelli and Doreen Hannes, editorial assistant Shana Milkie, publicist Gayle Loiselle, and cover designer Carol Kiser.

My wife, Jean, and children Laura and Jason have, as always, been important arbiters of taste in reviewing both copy and cover designs.

Notes

Introduction

1. Bill Marler, "Cantaloupe, a Deadly Fruit – Again." Marler Blog, August 17, 2012, http://www.marlerblog.com/legal-cases/cantaloupe-a-deadly-fruit-again/#.UwtgqHkzeAE.

2. David Gumpert, The Raw Milk Revolution: Behind America's Emerging Battle over Food Rights. White River Junction, Vermont: Chelsea Green Publishing, 2009. Available online at http://www.amazon.com/Raw-Milk-Revolution-Americas-Emerging/dp/1603582193/ref=sr_1_1_title_1_pap?s=books&ie=UTF8&qid=1412692455&sr=1-1&keywords=raw+milk+revolution.

3. David Gumpert, Life, Liberty, and the Pursuit of Food Rights: The Escalating Battle over Who Decides What We Eat. White River Junction, Vermont: Chelsea Green Publishing, 2013. Available online at http://www.amazon.com/Life-Liberty-Pursuit-Food-Rights/dp/1603584048/ref=cm_cr_pr_product_top.

Chapter 1. Raw Milk Basics

1. fairlife, LLC, partner of The Coca-Cola Company, http://fairlife.com/our-products/.

Chapter 2. Why All the Fuss?

1. Rebecca Riffkin, "Forty-five Percent of Americans Seek Out Organic Foods," Gallup poll, 2014, http://www.gallup.com/poll/174524/forty-five-percent-americans-seek-organic-foods.aspx.

2. David Gumpert, "Answer to This Q Is Litmus Test About Progress on Raw Milk Acceptance; MD Campaign; Upcoming Talks," The Complete Patient blog, January 20, 2012, http://thecompletepatient.com/article/2014/january/20/answer-q-litmus-test-about-progress-raw-milk-acceptance-md-campaign-upcoming.

3. "Food Safety Talk 55: Damn Ignorant PhDs," Food Safety Talk podcasts, February 9, 2014, http://foodsafetytalk.com/food-safety-talk/2014/2/8/food-safety-talk-55-damn-ignorant-phds.

4. Benjamin J. K. Davis et al., "A Literature Review of the Risks and Benefits of Consuming Raw and Pasteurized Cow's Milk," (A response to the request from the Maryland House of Delegates' Health and Government Operations Committee), December 8, 2014, http://thecompletepatient.com/sites/default/files/attachments/RawMilk-MD-JohnsHopkinsReport2014_1208%20.pdf

5. American Academy of Pediatrics, "American Academy of Pediatrics Advises Pregnant Women and Children Not to Consume Raw Milk Products," press release, December 16, 2013, http://www.aap.org/en-us/about-the-aap/aap-press-room/Pages/American-Academy-of-Pediatrics-Advises-Pregnant-Women-and-Children-Not-to-Consume-Raw-Milk-Products.aspx.

6. Trisha Robinson et al., "Raw Milk Consumption among Patients with Non–Outbreak-related Enteric Infections, Minnesota, USA, 2001–2010," Minnesota Department of Health, 2013, http://rawmilkinstitute.net/wp/wp-content/uploads/2013/12/minnesota_raw_milk_study.pdf.

7. Centers for Disease Control and Prevention (CDC), "Estimates of Foodborne Illness in the United States,"

Atlanta, Georgia: U.S. Department of Health and Human Services, Centers for Disease Control and Prevention, 2014, http://www.cdc.gov/foodborneburden/.

8. Hayden Stewart et al., "Why Are Americans Consuming Less Fluid Milk? A Look at Generational Differences in Intake Frequency," Economic Research Report Number 149, Economic Research Service, United States Department of Agriculture, May 2013, https://www.motherjones.com/files/err149-1.pdf.

9. David Gumpert, "We Can Feed the World, Says Ed Shank, As He Transitions from Feedlot to Organic Raw Dairy Operation," The Complete Patient blog, October 5, 2009, http://thecompletepatient.com/article/2009/october/5/we-can-feed-world-says-ed-shank-he-transitions-feedlot-organic-raw-dairy.

10. Centers for Disease Control and Prevention (CDC), Foodborne Active Surveillance Network (FoodNet) Population Survey Atlas of Exposures . Atlanta, Georgia: U.S. Department of Health and Human Services, Centers for Disease Control and Prevention, 2006-2007, http://www.cdc.gov/foodnet/surveys/FoodNetExposureAtlas0607_508.pdf.

11. www.mercola.com.

Chapter 4. How Risky Is Raw Milk, Really?

1. Centers for Disease Control and Prevention (CDC), "Real Stories of the Dangers of Raw Milk," last updated December 12, 2014, http://www.cdc.gov/foodsafety/rawmilk/raw-milk-videos.html.

2. Centers for Disease Control and Prevention (CDC), Foodborne Outbreak Online Database (FOOD) tool. Available online at http://wwwn.cdc.gov/foodborneoutbreaks/.

3. Ibid.

4. http://www.realrawmilkfacts.com/.

5. Real Raw Milk Facts working group, "Outbreaks from Foodborne Pathogens in Unpasteurized (Raw) Milk and Raw Milk Cheeses, United States 1998-present," last updated October 24, 2013, http://www.realrawmilkfacts.com/PDFs/Raw-Dairy-Outbreak-Table.pdf.

6. Real Raw Milk Facts working group, "Outbreaks from Foodborne Pathogens in Milk and Cheeses Sold as Pasteurized, United States 1998-present," last updated March 18, 2014, http://www.realrawmilkfacts.com/PDFs/pasteurized-dairy-outbreak-table.pdf.

7. Stephen Dinan, "Feds: Fresh milk 150 times more dangerous than pasteurized dairy." The Washington Times, February 21, 2012, http://www.washingtontimes.com/news/2012/feb/21/feds-fresh-milk-150-times-dangerous-pasteurized/.

8. Kiera Butler, "Is Raw Milk Really Good for You?" Mother Jones, September/October 2012, http://www.motherjones.com/environment/2012/09/is-raw-milk-safe-e-coli.

9. Deborah Blum, "The Raw-Milk Deal," Slate, July 19, 2010, http://www.slate.com/articles/life/food/2010/07/the_rawmilk_deal.html.

10. Centers for Disease Control and Prevention (CDC), "Raw Milk Question and Answers," last updated December

12, 2014, http://www.cdc.gov/foodsafety/rawmilk/raw-milk-questions-and-answers.html#prevent.

11. Ibid. http://www.cdc.gov/foodsafety/rawmilk/raw-milk-questions-and-answers.html#who.

12. Matthew Stasiewicz et al., "Responding to Bioterror Concerns by Increasing Milk Pasteurization Temperature Would Increase Estimated Annual Deaths from Listeriosis, " Journal of Food Protection, no. 5 (2014): 696-705, http://www.ingentaconnect.com/content/iafp/jfp/2014/00000077/00000005/art00001.

13. David Gumpert, "In Official Reports, You'd Never Know It Was Pasteurized Dairy Making People Sick," The Complete Patient blog, June 1, 2014, http://thecompletepatient.com/article/2014/june/1/official-reports-you%E2%80%99d-never-know-it-was-pasteurized-dairy-making-people-sick.

14. Kimberly Kindy, "Political Push for Raw, Unpasteurized Milk Is Increasing Access, but Illnesses Are up, Too, " The Washington Post, April 4, 2014, http://www.washingtonpost.com/politics/political-push-for-raw-unpasteurized-milk-is-increasing-access-but-illnesses-are-up-too/2014/04/04/e62bc884-b443-11e3-8020-b2d790b3c9e1_story.html.

15. Hannah Sentenac, "Raw Milk Movement Grows amid Push to Ease Regulation," Fox News, May 1, 2014, http://www.foxnews.com/leisure/2014/05/01/raw-milk-movement-grows-amid-push-to-ease-regulation/.

16. Centers for Disease Control and Prevention (CDC), Foodborne Outbreak Online Database (FOOD) tool. Available online at http://wwwn.cdc.gov/foodborneoutbreaks/.

17. Ibid.

18. Center for Science in the Public Interest, Outbreak Alert! Database. Available online at https://www.cspinet.org/foodsafety/outbreak/pathogen.php.

19. Center for Science in the Public Interest, "Reports of Foodborne-Illness Outbreaks Decline by 40%," March 25, 2013, http://www.cspinet.org/new/201303251.html.

20. Centers for Disease Control and Prevention (CDC), "Estimates of Foodborne Illness in the United States," Atlanta, Georgia: U.S. Department of Health and Human Services, Centers for Disease Control and Prevention, 2014, http://www.cdc.gov/foodborneburden/.

21. Marion Nestle, "CDC Halves Foodborne Illness Count. But Why Now?" Food Politics blog, December 16, 2010, http://www.foodpolitics.com/2010/12/cdc-halves-foodborne-illness-count-but-why-now/.

Chapter 5. What Are the Health Benefits of Raw Milk?

1. Ron Schmid, "Raw Milk - History, Health Benefits and Distortions: The Health Benefits of Raw Milk," http://www.drrons.com/raw-milk-history-health-benefits-distortions-4.htm.

2. Ibid.

3. http://www.realrawmilkfacts.com/.

4. Real Raw Milk Facts, "Hot Topics – Two Milks: Pasteurized and Raw," http://www.realrawmilkfacts.com/raw-milk-hot-topics.

5. Michigan Fresh Unprocessed Whole Milk Workgroup, Report of Michigan Fresh Unprocessed Whole Milk Workgroup, December 2012, http://cdn.modernfarmer.com/wp-content/uploads/2013/08/MI-FUWmilk.pdf.

6. " $6.9 Million Funds Studies of Health-Boosting Compounds in Cow's Milk," University of California, Davis press release, November 25, 2014, http://news.ucdavis.edu/search/news_detail.lasso?id=11099.

7. Mark Astley, "Raw Milk Consumption Reduces Risk of Infant Respiratory Infections: Study," Dairy Reporter, October 22, 2014, http://www.dairyreporter.com/R-D/Raw-milk-consumption-cuts-risk-of-infant-respiratory-infections-Study.

8. Sarah, the Healthy Home Economist, "Low Temp Pasteurized Milk Not a Good Sub for Raw Milk," The Health Home Economist blog, October 5, 2012, http://www.thehealthyhomeeconomist.com/low-temp-pasteurized-milk-not-a-good-sub-for-raw-milk/.

9. M. Waser et al., "Inverse Association of Farm Milk Consumption with Asthma and Allergy in Rural and Suburban Populations across Europe," Clinical and Experimental Allergy 5 (2007): 661–70, doi: 10.1111/j.1365-2222.2006.02640.x.

10. Georg Loss et al., "The Protective Effect of Farm Milk Consumption on Childhood Asthma and Atopy: The GABRIELA Study," Journal of Allergy and Clinical mmunology 128, no. 4 (2011): 766–73, http://www.acionline.org/article/S0091-6749%2811%2901234-6/abstract.

11. Georg Loss et al., "Consumption of Unprocessed

Cow's Milk Protects Infants from Common Respiratory Infections," Journal of Allergy and Clinical Immunology 135, no. 1 (2015): 56–62, doi: http://dx.doi.org/10.1016/j.jaci.2014.08.044.

12. Centers for Disease Control and Prevention (CDC), "Raw Milk Question and Answers," last updated December 12, 2014, http://www.cdc.gov/foodsafety/rawmilk/raw-milk-questions-and-answers.html#prevent.

13. Michael Landa, Director, Center for Food Safety and Applied Nutrition, letter to Mark McAfee denying Citizen Petition Docket No. FDA-2013-P-0701, November 25, 2014, http://thecompletepatient.com/sites/default/files/attachments/FDA-Citizen%20Petition%20response%20to%20Mr.%20McAfee.pdf.

14. Public Broadcasting System (PBS), Food Forward, Season 2, Episode 5: "Modern Milk," September 12, 2014, http://video.pbs.org/video/2365301485/.

15. L. E. Macdonald et al., "A Systematic Review and Meta-Analysis of the Effects of Pasteurization on Milk Vitamins, and Evidence for Raw Milk Consumption and Other Health-Related Outcomes," Journal of Food Protection 74, no. 11 (2011): 1814-32, doi: 10.4315/0362-028X.JFP-10-269, http://www.ncbi.nlm.nih.gov/pubmed/22054181.

16. "Proposed Options for the Sale of Raw Milk to Consumers," New Zealand Ministry for Primary Industries, http://www.foodsafety.govt.nz/elibrary/industry/raw-milk-sales-2014/index.htm.

17. Anna Petherick, "The Evidence Around Raw Milk," Splash! milk science update, October 2012, http://milkgenomics.org/article/the-evidence-around-raw-milk/.

18. S. Bashir and L. Y. Al-Ayadhi, "Effect of Camel Milk on Thymus and Activation-Regulated Chemokine in Autistic Children: Double-Blind Study," Pediatric Research 75, no. 4 (2014): 559-63, doi: 10.1038/pr.2013.248, http://www.ncbi.nlm.nih.gov/pubmed/24375082.

19. Christina Adams, "Patient Report: Autism Spectrum Disorder Treated with Camel Milk," Global Advances in Health and Medicine 2 no. 6 (2013): 78–80, doi: 10.7453/gahmj.2013.094, http://www.ncbi.nlm.nih.gov/pmc/articles/PMC3865381/.

20. Sarah Mummah et al., "Effect of Raw Milk on Lactose Intolerance: A Randomized Controlled Pilot Study," Annals of Family Medicine 12, no. 2 (2014): 134-141, doi: 10.1370/afm.1618, http://annfammed.org/content/12/2/134.full.

21. A. Høst and E. G. Samuelsson, "Allergic Reactions to Raw, Pasteurized, and Homogenized/Pasteurized Cow Milk: A Comparison. A Double-Blind Placebo-Controlled Study In Milk Allergic Children," Allergy 43, no. 2 (1988): 113-8, http://www.ncbi.nlm.nih.gov/m/pubmed/3284399/?i=15&from=pasteurized%20milk%20allergies.

22. F. Roth-Walter et al., "Pasteurization of Milk Proteins Promotes Allergic Sensitization by Enhancing Uptake Through Peyer's Patches," Allergy 63, no. 7 (2008): 882-90, doi: 10.1111/j.1398-9995.2008.01673.x, http://www.ncbi.nlm.nih.gov/m/pubmed/18588554/.

23. Judith Lipton, "Is There a Cure for Crohn's Disease?" Psychology Today Pura Vida blog, November 10, 2013, http://www.psychologytoday.com/blog/pura-vida/201311/is-there-cure-crohns-disease.

24. Travis Thompson, Facebook post, December 22, 2013, https://www.facebook.com/travisthompsonmn/posts/3832940199784.

Chapter 6. Reconcile the Risks and Benefits of Raw Milk

1. Chelsea Washington, "State Health Department Confirms Five Cases of E. Coli," Fox 25 KOKH-TV, April 4, 2014, http://www.okcfox.com/story/25168618/state-health-department-confirms-five-people-are-infected-with-a-deadly-strain-of-ecoli.

2. Chris Kresser, "Raw Milk Reality: Is Raw Milk Dangerous?" May 9, 2012, http://chriskresser.com/raw-milk-reality-is-raw-milk-dangerous.

3. U.S. Department of Transportation, "Accidental Deaths - United States - 1999-2003," January 1, 2004, http://phmsa dot.gov/portal/site/PHMSA/

4. Center for Science in the Public Interest, Outbreak Alert! 2014: A Review of Foodborne Illness in America from 2002-2011, April 2014, http://cspinet.org/reports/outbreakalert2014.pdf.

5. Center for Science in the Public Interest, "Reports of Foodborne-Illness Outbreaks Decline by 40%," March 25, 2013, http://www.cspinet.org/new/201303251.html.

6. Centers for Disease Control and Prevention (CDC), "Raw Milk Question and Answers," last updated December 12, 2014, http://www.cdc.gov/foodsafety/rawmilk/raw-milk-questions-and-answers.html.

7. Centers for Disease Control and Prevention (CDC),

"Majority of Dairy-Related Disease Outbreaks Linked to Raw Milk," press release, February 21, 2012, http://www.cdc.gov/media/releases/2012/p0221_raw_milk_outbreak.html.

8. Ted Beals, "Those Pathogens, What You Should Know," Weston A. Price Foundation Campaign for Real Milk, July 31, 2011, http://www.realmilk.com/safety/those-pathogens-what-you-should-know/.

9. Chris Kresser, "Raw Milk Reality: Is Raw Milk Dangerous?" May 9, 2012, http://chriskresser.com/raw-milk-reality-is-raw-milk-dangerous.

10. James T C Li, "Does Childhood Exposure to Germs Help Prevent Asthma?" Mayo Clinic, April 9, 2013, http://www.mayoclinic.org/diseases-conditions/childhood-asthma/expert-answers/hygiene-hypothesis/faq-20058102.

11. Centers for Disease Control and Prevention (CDC), "Real Stories of the Dangers of Raw Milk," last updated December 12, 2014, http://www.cdc.gov/foodsafety/rawmilk/raw-milk-videos.html.

12. http://rawmilkinstitute.net/.

13. Elizabeth Mungai et al., "Increased Outbreaks Associated with Nonpasteurized Milk, United States, 2007–2012," Emerging Infectious Diseases 21 no. 1 (2015), http://dx.doi.org/10.3201/eid2101.140447.

14. "E. coli O157:H7 and Salmonella typhimurium DT104: The Role of Animals," University of Wisconsin-Madison School of Veterinary Medicine, Zoonotic Diseases Tutorials, last updated December 30, 2004, http://www.vetmed.wisc.edu/pbs/zoonoses/o157dt104/

o157dt104index.html.

Chapter 7. How Do I Go About Buying Raw Milk?

1. http://www.realmilk.com.

2. Farm-to-Consumer Legal Defense Fund, "State-by-State Review of Raw Milk Laws," June 21, 2013, http://www.farmtoconsumer.org/raw_milk_map.htm.

3. http://www.realmilk.com.

4. https://www.farmmatch.com/.

5. http://www.realmilk.com.

Chapter 8. How Do I Find the Safest Raw Milk?

1. Raw Milk Institute, Mission Statement, http://rawmilkinstitute.net/about-rawmi/mission-statement/.

2. Farm-to-Consumer Foundation, Raw Milk Production Handbook and Chore Time (DVD), http://f2cfnd.org/farm-to-consumer-foundation-news/ftcf-now-provides-free-downloads-of-our-raw-milk-guidebook-and-dvd/.

Chapter 9. How Do I Find the Best Quality Raw Milk?

1. Weston A. Price Foundation, "Find a Local Chapter," last updated May 14, 2014, http://www.westonaprice.org/get-involved/find-local-chapter/.

Chapter 10. Bringing Raw Milk Into Your Home... Peacefully

1. Nok-Noi Ricker, "DHHS Accused of Abusing Authority with Brooklin Teen Who Feeds Baby Goat Milk Formula," Bangor Daily News, September 5, 2013, http://

bangordailynews.com/2013/09/05/news/bangor/group-protests-dhhs-overreach-of-authority-involving-brooklin-teen-who-feeds-her-baby-homemade-goat-milk-formula-avoids-vaccines/.

2. Rebecca Riffkin, "Forty-five Percent of Americans Seek Out Organic Foods," Gallup poll, 2014, http://www.gallup.com/poll/174524/forty-five-percent-americans-seek-organic-foods.aspx.

3. Kiera Butler, "Is Raw Milk Really Good for You?" Mother Jones, September/October 2012, http://www.motherjones.com/environment/2012/09/is-raw-milk-safe-e-coli.

4. Dana Goodyear, "Raw Deal: California Cracks Down on an Underground Gourmet Club," The New Yorker, April 30, 2012, http://www.newyorker.com/magazine/2012/04/30/raw-deal.

5. American Academy of Pediatrics, "American Academy of Pediatrics Advises Pregnant Women and Children Not to Consume Raw Milk Products," press release, December 16, 2013, http://www.aap.org/en-us/about-the-aap/aap-press-room/Pages/American-Academy-of-Pediatrics-Advises-Pregnant-Women-and-Children-Not-to-Consume-Raw-Milk-Products.aspx.